Book 2

Activity Book

Book Staff and Contributors

Beth Zemble *Director, Alternative Learning Strategies; Director, English Language Arts*
Marianne Murphy *Content Specialist*
Anna Day *Senior Instructional Designer*
Cheryl Howard, Jenn Marrewa, Frances Suazo *Instructional Designers*
Mary Beck Desmond *Senior Text Editor*
Ron Stanley *Text Editors*
Suzanne Montazer *Creative Director, Print and ePublishing*
Jayoung Cho *Senior Print Visual Designer*
Eunice Corbin, Raymond MacDonald *Print Visual Designers*
Stephanie Shaw Williams *Cover Designer*
Amy Eward *Senior Manager, Writers*
Susan Raley *Senior Manager, Editors*
Julie Cacal *Project Coordinator*

Maria Szalay *Senior Vice President, Product Development*
John Holdren *Senior Vice President, Content and Curriculum*
David Pelizzari *Vice President, Content and Curriculum*
Kim Barcas *Vice President, Creative*
Laura Seuschek *Vice President, Instructional Design and Evaluation & Research*
Aaron Hall *Vice President, Program Management*

Lisa Dimaio Iekel *Senior Production Manager*

Credits

All illustrations © K12 unless otherwise noted
Ladybug. © Eyewire/Getty Images

About K12 Inc.

K12 Inc., a technology-based education company, is the nation's leading provider of proprietary curriculum and online education programs to students in grades K–12. K[12] provides its curriculum and academic services to online schools, traditional classrooms, blended school programs, and directly to families. K12 Inc. also operates the K[12] International Academy, an accredited, diploma-granting online private school serving students worldwide. K[12]'s mission is to provide any child the curriculum and tools to maximize success in life, regardless of geographic, financial, or demographic circumstances. K12 Inc. is accredited by CITA. More information can be found at www.K12.com.

ISBN-13: 978-1-60153-167--4
ISBN-10: 1-60153-167-2
Printed by RR Donnelley, Roanoke, VA, USA, October 2011, Lot102011

Contents

Literature & Comprehension

Revolution

Quilting Stories

Pet Poems

Bears

Clever Animals

Going to the Dogs

Writing Skills

Adjectives

Write Descriptively

Adverbs

Possessive Nouns

Write About Literature

Write About Information

Semester Review and Checkpoint

Revise and Publish Your Work

Literature & Comprehension

Check Your Reading

Introduce "Independence Day"

Reading Questions

Choose the answer.

1. What country ruled the 13 colonies?
   - **A.** France
   - **B.** America
   - **C.** England
   - **D.** Scotland

2. Which of the following did King George III do that made the colonists unhappy?
   - **A.** He made them pay taxes on tea.
   - **B.** He made them have their own army.
   - **C.** He made them keep their own weapons.
   - **D.** He made them buy things printed on paper.

3. What does the author say was one reason that the colonists were unhappy?
   - **A.** They wanted to live in England.
   - **B.** They thought the taxes were unfair.
   - **C.** They thought there should be more rules.
   - **D.** They wanted to have more tea sent from England.

4. What did the colonists do to let King George know they were angry?
   - **A.** They made their own taxes.
   - **B.** They refused to join the British army.
   - **C.** They went to England and told the king.
   - **D.** They threw English tea into Boston Harbor.

5. Which sentence is a fact from the article ?
   - **A.** America used to be 13 colonies.
   - **B.** King George III of England was very bad.
   - **C.** America is a better country than England.
   - **D.** The colonists had a right to be angry and throw tea away.

Reading for Meaning

Review "Independence Day"

Cause and Effect

Read the cause. Fill in the missing effect.

Cause	Effect
King George sent more Redcoats to the colonies.	The colonists
The Redcoats marched toward Lexington and Concord.	The Minutemen
The colonists signed the Declaration of Independence.	America

LITERATURE & COMPREHENSION

Check Your Reading

Introduce *Sam the Minuteman*

Reading Questions

Choose the answer.

1. Which best describes how the colonists feel about the British soldiers?
   - **A.** They are proud to have the soldiers in town.
   - **B.** They do not like the soldiers.
   - **C.** They think the soldiers are friendly.
   - **D.** They think the soldiers are funny.

2. How do Sam and his friend John feel when they go with the Minuteman to meet the British soldiers on their way to Concord ?
   - **A.** afraid
   - **B.** excited
   - **C.** happy
   - **D.** angry

3. Why does Captain Parker tell his Minutemen to move away when he sees the British soldiers coming?
   - **A.** He wants his Minutemen to hide and surprise the British.
   - **B.** Captain Parker and the Minutemen want to trick the British.
   - **C.** There are too many British soldiers for the Minutemen to fight.
   - **D.** He wants them to listen to what the British soldiers tell them.

LITERATURE & COMPREHENSION

4. How does Sam feel about what happens to his friend John?

   A. He is surprised that John runs away.

   B. He is happy that John is a good fighter.

   C. He is sad that John does not want to fight.

   D. He is angry that John is shot in the leg.

5. What does Sam do when he hears that the British soldiers are coming back ?

   A. He runs and hides in the barn.

   B. He goes to tell his friend John.

   C. He runs out with his gun to fight them.

   D. He helps his mother pack their things to leave.

Explore *Sam the Minuteman* (A)

Sequence of Events

Think about the sequence of events. Fill in each box with a part of the story.

Main Characters, Setting
There are British soldiers whom the colonists
Sam and his friend John go
Sam's friend John
Sam feels
When the British come back, Sam
The Minutemen and the colonists
The fight is the beginning of

Explore *Sam the Minuteman* (B)

Character Web

Write a trait for Sam in the center of the web. In the outer circles, write examples from the story that show the trait.

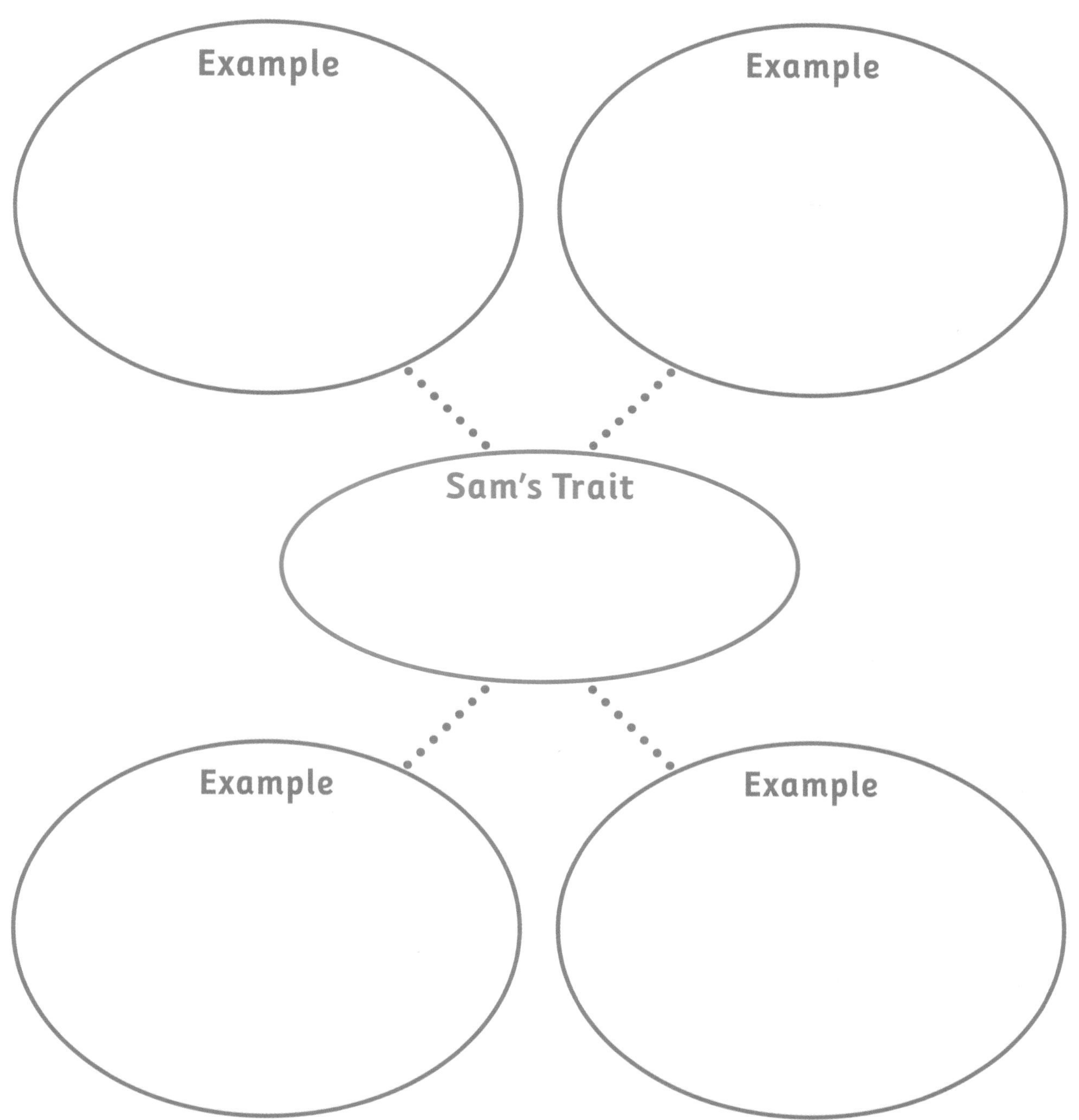

Reading for Meaning

Review *Sam the Minuteman*

Conflict and Resolution

Fill in the conflict and its resolution to complete the chart. The first row has been done for you.

Who is the conflict between?	What is the conflict about?	What is the resolution?
Sam and the British soldiers	The soldiers tell Sam to leave, but Sam does not leave fast enough.	The British soldiers shoot at Sam and the Minutemen.
Sam and his mother	Sam's mother wants him to stay home, but Sam	Sam
Sam and the British the second time they meet	Sam and the Minutemen want to stop the soldiers, but the soldiers want to	Sam and the Minutemen

LITERATURE & COMPREHENSION

Check Your Reading

Introduce *The Josefina Story Quilt*

Reading Questions

Choose the answer.

1. What does Pa say will happen to Josefina if she causes trouble on the trip?
   - **A.** They will give her to another family.
   - **B.** She will have to stay in her cage.
   - **C.** She will be put out of the wagon.
   - **D.** They will sell her for money or food.

2. While riding along the trail, what does Faith work on?
   - **A.** writing a diary about the trip
   - **B.** sewing new clothes for herself
   - **C.** making meals over the campfire
   - **D.** making a patchwork quilt

3. How does Josefina cause trouble along the trail?
   - **A.** She falls into the river.
   - **B.** She chases a horse.
   - **C.** She refuses to lay eggs.
   - **D.** She wakes everyone at night.

4. What does Josefina do when robbers sneak into the camp?

   A. She chases the robbers and pecks them.

   B. She makes a lot of noise, and the robbers run away.

   C. She watches them, and then she lays an egg.

   D. She sleeps quietly and doesn't hear a thing.

5. Why does Faith sew a pine tree patch on her quilt ?

   A. to remember her favorite place on the journey

   B. to remember what kinds of trees they saw on the trip

   C. to remember the place where they buried Josefina

   D. to remember Josefina's favorite tree

Explore *The Josefina Story Quilt* (A)

Faith's Feelings for Josefina

Complete the sentences. Cut out the shape and fold along the lines. Glue or tape the tabs.

Faith worries about leaving

Faith wants to take

Faith loves Josefina like

Faith and Josefina understand each other like

Faith cries when

Draw a picture of Faith and Josefina.

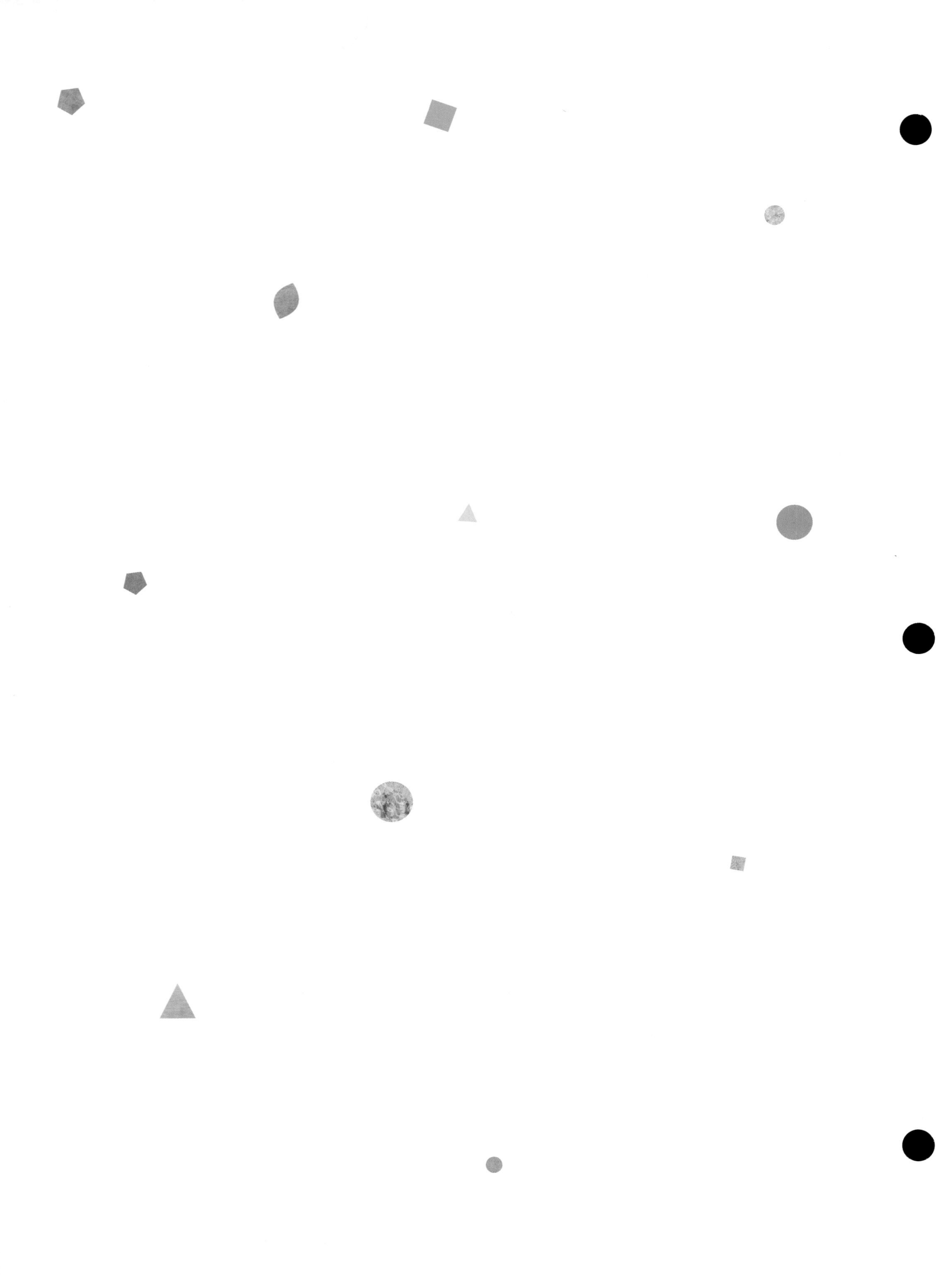

Explore *The Josefina Story Quilt* (B)

Conflict and Resolution

Answer the question.

1. Between whom is the conflict in the story?

2. What is the conflict about?

3. Name three events during the trip that show the conflict.

4. How is the conflict resolved?

Making Connections

Review *The Josefina Story Quilt*

The Theme in My Life

LITERATURE & COMPREHENSION

Write your response.

1. The theme of *The Josefina Story Quilt* is ______________________

____

____

____

____

2. Write a story about a person, thing, or event in your life that is important to you and explain why it is important to remember it.

____

____

____

____

____

____

Check Your Reading

Introduce "Pioneer Patchwork"

Reading Questions

Choose the answer.

1. What is the topic of this article?
   - **A.** pioneer life in the West
   - **B.** pioneer patchwork quilts
   - **C.** pioneer women and their jobs
   - **D.** pioneer clothing and styles

2. What is the main idea of the article?
   - **A.** Pioneer women saved old clothes.
   - **B.** Pioneer women knew how to sew.
   - **C.** Pioneer women made patchwork quilts.
   - **D.** Pioneer women did their work together.

3. Which detail supports the main idea?
   - **A.** Hannah Will was a pioneer girl who was very good at sewing.
   - **B.** Many quilt patterns had names, such as Broken Dishes.
   - **C.** The life of pioneers was hard.
   - **D.** Pioneer women used scraps of old clothes to make quilts.

LITERATURE & COMPREHENSION

4. Look at the diagram on page 21 of "Pioneer Patchwork." Which part of the quilt goes in the middle?

   A. the backing

   B. the batting

   C. the pattern

   D. the patchwork

5. Read the following steps in making a quilt. Which step should come before the last step?

   > Choose a design. Cut fabric into small squares. Stitch the large fabric squares together to make the top.

   A. Sew the small fabric squares into bigger squares.

   B. Put together the top, the batting, and the backing.

   C. Sew the three parts of the quilt together.

   D. Choose fabric squares in colors that you like.

Review "Pioneer Patchwork"

Steps in Process

Write the steps of the process to make a quilt in sequence.

1. Pioneer women started a quilt by ______________________________

____

2. They chose the fabric from ______________________________

____

3. They cut ______________________________

____

4. They sewed ______________________________

____

5. They sewed the bigger squares ______________________________

____

6. They put batting in between ______________________________

____

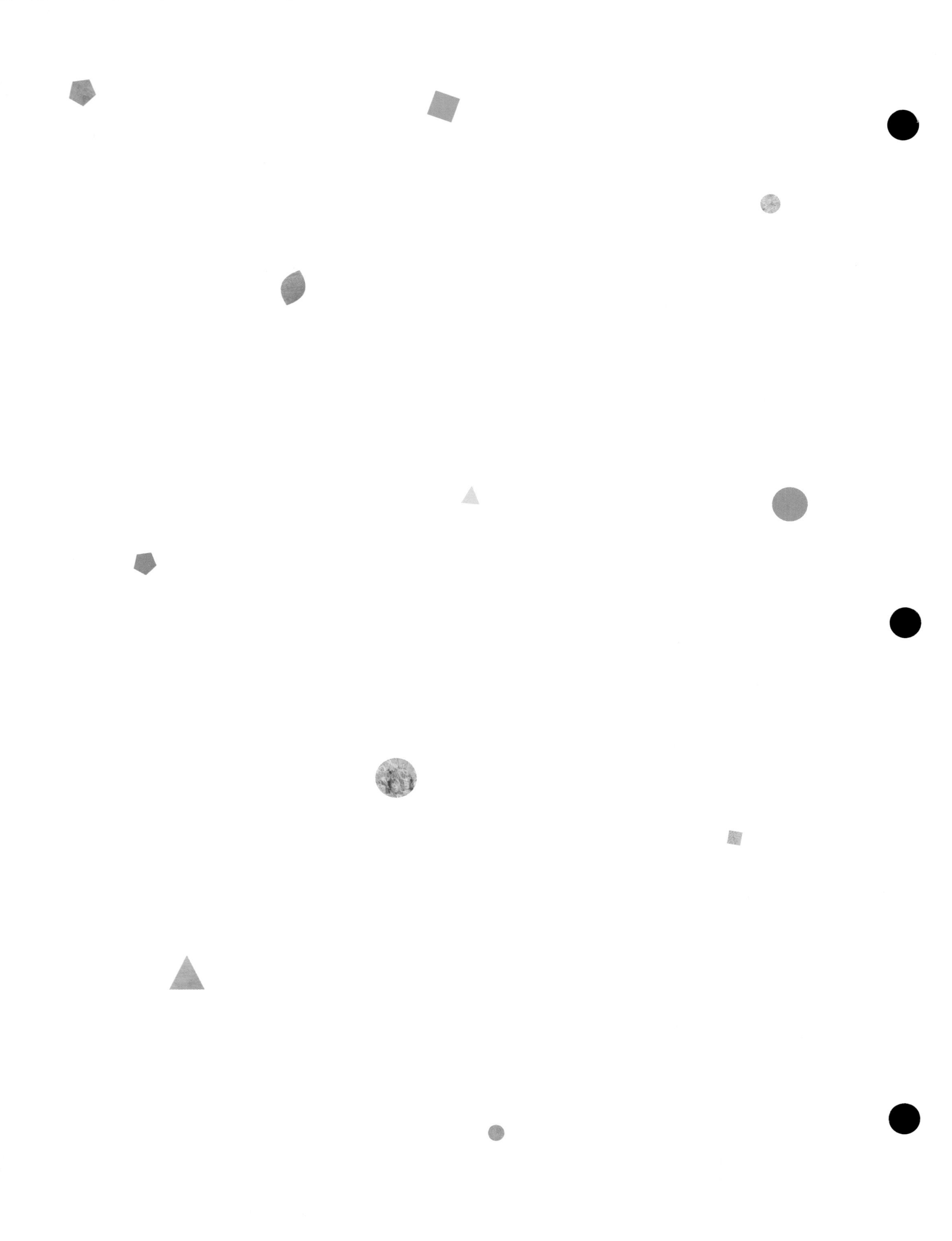

Check Your Reading

Introduce Pet Poems

Reading Questions

Choose the answer.

1. In "Who to Pet and Who Not to," which does the speaker say **not** to pet?

   A. dog

   B. cat

   C. worm

   D. porcupine

2. In "Who to Pet and Who Not to," what does it mean when the speaker asks, "You want to be a cactus?"

   A. If you like porcupines, you must like cactus plants.

   B. If you pet a porcupine, you'll get its quills stuck on you.

   C. If you don't like pets, you could pretend to be a cactus.

   D. If you have a pet porcupine, you must live in the desert.

3. Why does the speaker in "Hamsters" think hamsters are "the nicest things"?

   A. They like dogs.

   B. They have soft fur.

   C. They are happy.

   D. They like to be alone.

LITERATURE & COMPREHENSION

4. Why might the speaker in "Hamsters" like fitting a hamster inside a pocket?
   A. because a hamster can go wherever you go
   B. because a hamster can sneak out to scare people
   C. because a hamster doesn't need to go for walks on a leash
   D. because a hamster can hide from animals that want to harm it

Introduce Pet Poems

Read Poetry Aloud

Complete this checklist for poems you read aloud.

Did you...	Poem 1	Poem 2
Practice reading the poem to yourself?		
Pause for commas and periods?		
Use your voice to ask questions?		
Use your voice to show exclamations?		
Read slowly and clearly?		
Use a normal voice?		

Read

Poetry Reading Strategies Guide

Follow these strategies to help you read and understand poetry.

Before You Read

1. Do a Book Walk.
   - Read the title.
   - Look at the pictures.
   - Look at the shape of the poem. Look at the lines, stanzas, and punctuation.
2. Predict what you will read about.

During Reading

1. Read the poem once silently to yourself.
2. Pause only at punctuation, not at the ends of the lines.
3. Make sure you know what every word means.
4. Read the poem a second time aloud.
5. Listen for rhyming words and rhythm.
6. Try to imagine what the poet is talking about.
7. Ask yourself: What are the topic, feelings, or ideas in this poem?

After Reading

1. Ask questions.
   - How does the speaker feel about the topic, feelings, or ideas in this poem?
   - What words are used to describe the topics, feelings, or ideas?

LITERATURE & COMPREHENSION

- Are there images?
- Do the images remind me of anything I know?
- Are there any special words that stand out?
- What does the poet want me to imagine or feel?

2. When you don't understand something, repair your reading with a strategy.
   - **Summarize:** Tell yourself in one or two sentences what the poem is about.
   - **Make inferences:** Use what you know to understand what you read.
   - **Reread:** Read again, a little more slowly to make sure you don't miss something.
   - **Use context clues:** Look for clues nearby new words to help you define them.
   - **Ask for help:** If you have a question and can't find the answer, ask for help.

Introduce More Pet Poems

Reading Questions

Choose the answer.

1. In the poem "My Dog," why does the dog bark?

   A. He is afraid of sirens.

   B. He doesn't like cats.

   C. He wants people to notice him.

   D. He wants to bark.

2. In the poem "My Dog," why are the words *at* and *wanted* in italic?

   A. because they rhyme with other words in the poem

   B. because italic shows that these words are important

   C. because they are describing words

   D. because they show how the speaker feels

3. In the poem "My Kitten," to whom is the speaker talking?

   A. a friend

   B. her mother

   C. her kitten

   D. no one

4. In the poem "My Kitten," how does the speaker feel about her kitten?

   A. She likes to play ball with it.

   B. She loves it.

   C. She thinks it is funny.

   D. She feels sad when she is not with it.

LITERATURE & COMPREHENSION

Check Your Reading

Introduce "The Foolish Goose"

Reading Questions

Choose the answer.

1. Who does Gray Goose meet first?
   - **A.** White Crane
   - **B.** Brownie Hen
   - **C.** Wise Old Crow
   - **D.** the Farmer

2. What does Wise Old Crow tell Gray Goose to do?
   - **A.** spread his corn on the ground to make it go a long way
   - **B.** swim out in a lake to see pearls and diamonds
   - **C.** throw his corn on the road to see strange sights
   - **D.** put some corn in the ground so it will grow into corn plants

3. Why does White Crane tell Gray Goose to swim out in the lake?
   - **A.** to see strange sights
   - **B.** to see pearls and diamonds
   - **C.** to make his corn go a long way
   - **D.** to make his corn grow into plants

LITERATURE & COMPREHENSION

4. Why does Gray Goose throw his corn on the road?
   A. White Crane tells him he'll see pearls and diamonds.
   B. Wise Old Crow tells he it will make his corn go a long way.
   C. The Farmer tells him it will help his corn grow into plants.
   D. Brownie Hen tells him he'll see strange sights.

5. Who gives Gray Goose the best advice?
   A. White Crane
   B. Wise Old Crow
   C. the Farmer
   D. Brownie Hen

Introduce "The Foolish Goose"

Choices and Consequences

Fill in the missing choice or consequence.

Gray Goose's Choice	Consequence of His Choice
	Wise Old Crow eats some of his corn.
He listens to White Crane and swims out in the lake.	
	Brownie Hen eats some of his corn.

Reading for Meaning

Explore "The Foolish Goose"

Character Traits and Lessons

Answer the question.

1. What happens each time Gray Goose chooses to listen to an animal?

____

2. How would you describe Gray Goose when he listens to the animals?

____

3. What does Gray Goose do when the Farmer tells him to plant the corn?

____

4. What happens when Gray Goose plants the corn?

____

5. How would you describe Gray Goose after his corn has grown?

____

6. What lesson has Gray Goose learned?

____

____

LITERATURE & COMPREHENSION

Check Your Reading

Introduce Poems About the Natural World

Reading Questions

Choose the answer.

1. What is the rhyme scheme for the first stanza of the poem "Discovery"?
   - **A.** The rhyme scheme is AABB.
   - **B.** The rhyme scheme is ABCB.
   - **C.** The rhyme scheme is ABAB.
   - **D.** The rhyme scheme is ABCD.

2. In the poem "Discovery," what do the speaker and his friend Joe find under a rock?
   - **A.** tadpoles
   - **B.** lichens
   - **C.** ferns
   - **D.** salamanders

3. In the poem "Hurt No Living Thing," which is an example of personification?
   - **A.** dancing gnat
   - **B.** dusty wing
   - **C.** light grasshopper
   - **D.** beetle fat

LITERATURE & COMPREHENSION

4. In the poem "Hurt No Living Thing," why does the poet talk about insects?

   A. She thinks insects are the only animals that should not be hurt.

   B. She thinks insects should not be allowed to hurt people.

   C. She thinks people should not hurt any creature, even small insects.

   D. She thinks readers would only want to read a poem about insects.

5. In the poem "Hurt No Living Thing," how does the speaker feel about insects?

   A. fearful

   B. worried

   C. sad

   D. caring

Explore Poems About the Natural World

Poetic Language

Write the rhyme scheme. Circle the examples of alliteration. Underline three images.

Hurt No Living Thing

by Christina Rossetti

Hurt no living thing; A
Ladybird, nor butterfly, B
Nor moth with dusty wing, ______
Nor cricket chirping cheerily, ______
Nor grasshopper so light of leap, ______
Nor dancing gnat, nor beetle fat, ______
Nor harmless worms that creep. ______

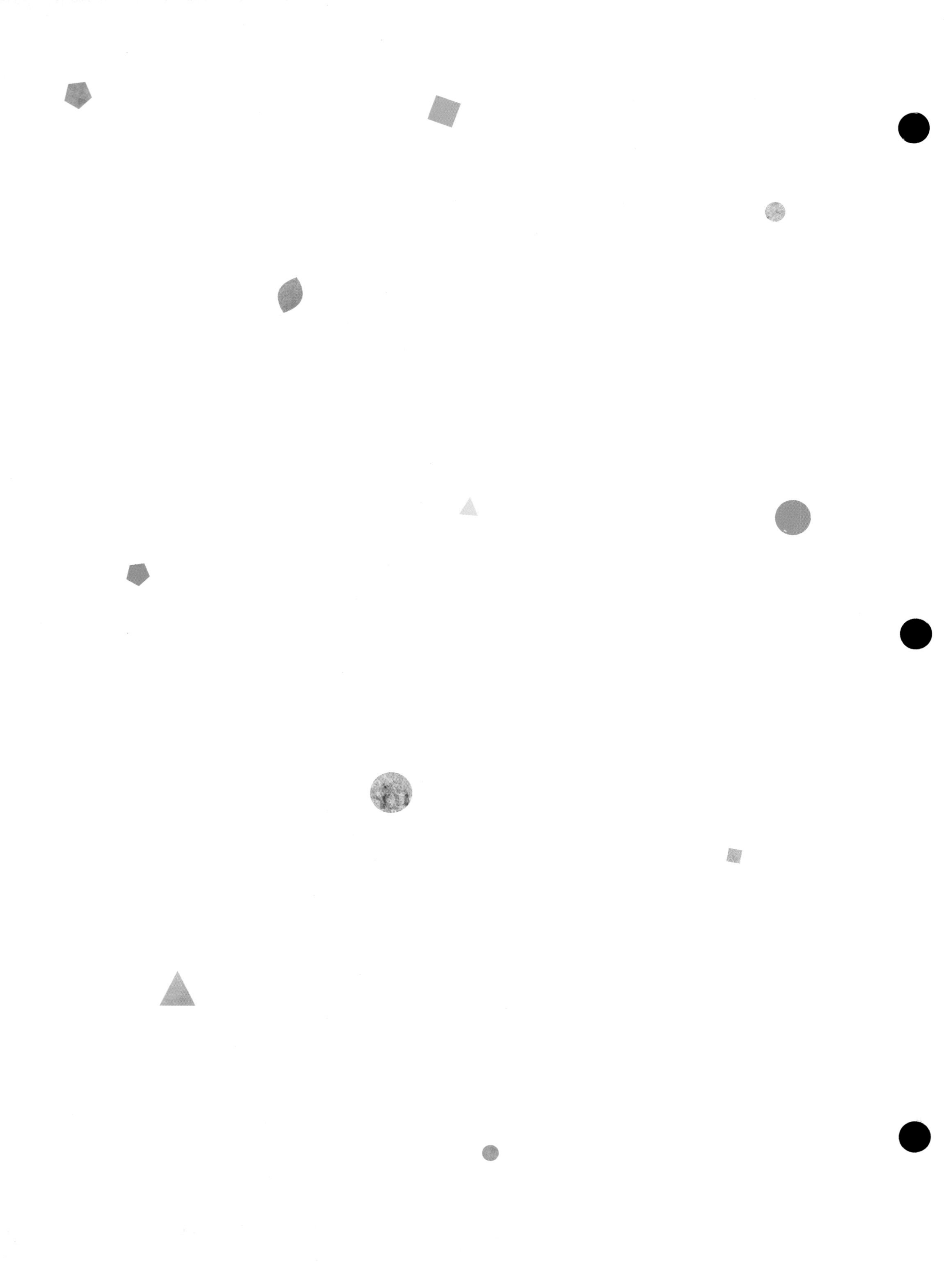

Check Your Reading

Introduce *Cam Jansen: The Mystery of the Stolen Diamonds*

Reading Questions

Choose the answer.

1. Why is Jennifer called "The Camera," or Cam for short?
   - **A.** She loves cameras.
   - **B.** She always carries a camera.
   - **C.** Her memory is like a camera.
   - **D.** She always wears a cameo pin.

2. What is the name of Cam's friend?
   - **A.** Howie
   - **B.** Eric
   - **C.** Ben
   - **D.** Mark

3. How does Cam know that something has happened at the jewelry store?
   - **A.** People in the mall start yelling.
   - **B.** The store alarm goes off.
   - **C.** A couple leaves the store.
   - **D.** The police arrive at the mall.

LITERATURE & COMPREHENSION

LITERATURE & COMPREHENSION

4. Whom does Cam think the police need to catch?
   - **A.** the couple with the baby
   - **B.** the old woman using a cane
   - **C.** the man in the dark suit
   - **D.** the woman who was knocked down

5. Why does Cam say "Click" to remember the young couple?
   - **A.** They left the store right after the man in the dark suit.
   - **B.** They were carrying a baby, and Cam likes babies.
   - **C.** They looked like people she knew from her neighborhood.
   - **D.** They were not hurrying like the man in the dark suit.

Check Your Reading

Explore *Cam Jansen: The Mystery of the Stolen Diamonds* (A)

Reading Questions

Choose the answer.

1. What did the robber make Mr. Parker do?
   - **A.** face the wall
   - **B.** lie down on the floor
   - **C.** hold his hands in the air
   - **D.** put the diamonds in a bag

2. Why didn't the old women see the robber leave the store?
   - **A.** They were facing the wall.
   - **B.** They had closed their eyes.
   - **C.** They were too scared to look.
   - **D.** They were lying down on the floor.

3. What do the old women say about the man who ran from the store?
   - **A.** He had a partner.
   - **B.** He was the robber.
   - **C.** He wasn't the robber.
   - **D.** He helped Mr. Parker.

LITERATURE & COMPREHENSION

LITERATURE & COMPREHENSION

4. Why do Cam and Eric think it's strange that the man leaves the mall through the nearest exit?

   A. The man doesn't go in the same direction as he ran before.

   B. The man is going toward the parking lot, and he doesn't have a car.

   C. The man is heading straight for the police cars parked outside.

   D. The man leaves even though the police want to talk to him more.

5. Why does Cam want to follow the man instead of calling the police?

   A. She doesn't think the police do a very good job.

   B. She doesn't want to get in trouble for calling the police.

   C. She wants to find out if there is a reason to call the police.

   D. She hopes to get a reward if she catches the robber herself.

Explore *Cam Jansen: The Mystery of the Stolen Diamonds* (A)

Play Detective

Use clues to help solve the mystery. Write clues you find in the book and record your prediction.

Mystery

Who stole the diamonds from Parker's Jewelry Store?

Chapters 1 & 2

Clues	My prediction
1.	
2.	

Chapters 3, 4, & 5

Clues	Cam's conclusion
1.	
2.	

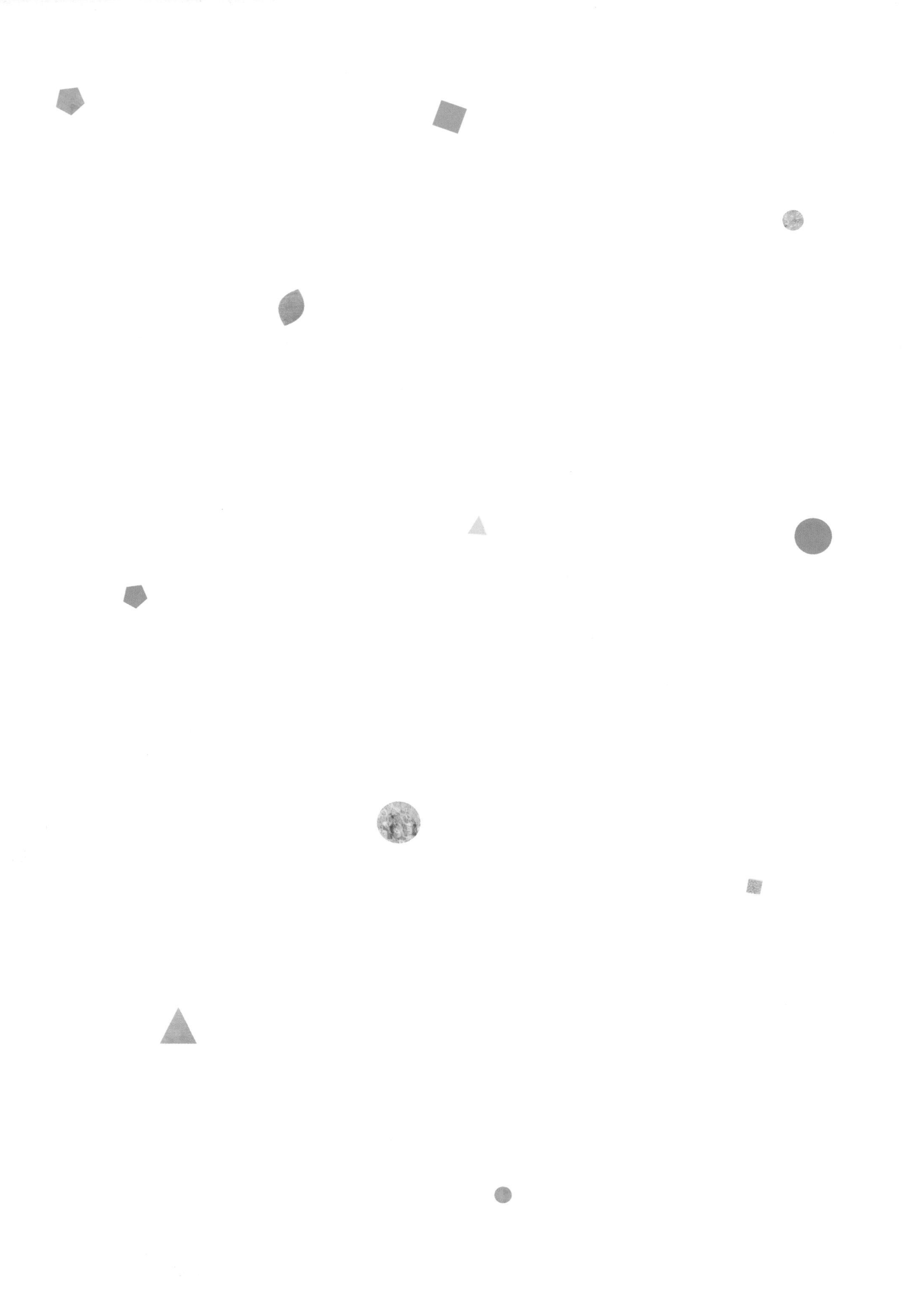

Explore *Cam Jansen: The Mystery of the Stolen Diamonds* (B)

Reading Questions

Choose the answer.

1. Which word best describes how Cam feels when she sees the diamonds?
   - **A.** angry
   - **B.** amazed
   - **C.** happy
   - **D.** scared

2. How does Cam trick the robbers?
   - **A.** She tells them she has called the police.
   - **B.** She slams a door to make them think she has left, and then she hides.
   - **C.** She says she needs to change Howie's diaper.
   - **D.** She says she knows where to get more diamonds.

3. How does Cam keep Howie from crying?
   - **A.** She rocks him back and forth.
   - **B.** She gives him his bottle to drink.
   - **C.** She gives him her finger to suck on.
   - **D.** She sings a song until he goes to sleep.

4. Why were the police confused by the robbery?

   A. They thought there was only one robber, and there were three.

   B. They followed the robbers down the wrong road to a different house.

   C. They thought Cam and Eric were with the robbers when they weren't.

   D. They thought the two old women were part of the robbers' plan.

Explore *Cam Jansen: The Mystery of the Stolen Diamonds* (B)

Solve the Mystery: How Did They Do It?

Fill in the boxes to explain how the robbers stole the diamonds.

Beginning

A man tells Mr. Parker to give up all his diamonds.

First Event

The robber

Second Event

The robber puts the diamonds in a baby rattle. Then, he

Third Event

The man in the dark suit runs out of the store and

Review *Cam Jansen: The Mystery of the Stolen Diamonds*

Cam's Character

Fill in the boxes.

Evidence from the Story	What This Tells Me About Cam	Cam's Character Trait
Cam has a photographic memory.		
Cam tells Eric she doesn't know much about babies.		
Cam follows the man in the dark suit to an abandoned house and waits for Eric to bring back help.		

Introduce "Bears in Danger"

Reading Questions

Choose the answer.

1. What is the main idea of the article?
   - **A.** There are only about 3,000 Andean bears in the world today.
   - **B.** Scientists want to learn more about sun bears and the best ways to help them.
   - **C.** Many kinds of bears in the world are in danger of becoming extinct.
   - **D.** People who know about bears are the only people who don't hurt bears.

2. Which detail supports the main idea?
   - **A.** Giant pandas live high in the mountains of China and eat mostly bamboo.
   - **B.** Polar bears may not be able to survive if the ice at the North Pole melts.
   - **C.** Even though sloth bears rarely attack humans, many people are afraid of them.
   - **D.** Parks and sanctuaries are nice places to see bears.

3. In what part of the world do sun bears live?
   - **A.** South America
   - **B.** North Pole
   - **C.** China
   - **D.** Southeast Asia

4. Which bears are losing their homes because people are cutting down forests where the bears live?
   - **A.** polar bears and giant pandas
   - **B.** polar bears and sloth bears
   - **C.** sloth bears and Andean bears
   - **D.** sun bears and Andean bears

5. What is one way that people are trying to save bears that are in danger?
   - **A.** capturing bear cubs to make them pets
   - **B.** passing laws to protect bears and their homes
   - **C.** killing dangerous bears so the safe ones can live
   - **D.** cutting down forests so bears will move to other places

Reading for Meaning

Review "Bears in Danger"

Organize Information

Complete the chart with facts from the article.

Kind of Bear	Bear's Home	Danger Bear Faces

Introduce *The Bears on Hemlock Mountain*

Reading Questions

Choose the answer.

1. What does Jonathan like to do with animals?
   - **A.** He likes to give them cookies.
   - **B.** He likes to throw sticks at them.
   - **C.** He likes to feed them and watch them.
   - **D.** He likes to make a noise and scare them.

2. Which word best describes Jonathan's mother?
   - **A.** shy
   - **B.** kind
   - **C.** bossy
   - **D.** nervous

3. When did Uncle James say he saw a bear on Hemlock Mountain?
   - **A.** He had seen bears all the time on Hemlock Mountain.
   - **B.** He had seen a bear the year before he told Jonathan.
   - **C.** He had seen a bear a few days before he told Jonathan.
   - **D.** He had seen a bear before Jonathan was born.

4. What does Jonathan's mother ask him to do?

   A. go get an iron pot from his aunt

   B. go to the store for more flour

   C. build a fire in the fireplace

   D. help her make cookies

5. Which word best describes how Jonathan feels about the task his mother sends him to do?

   A. proud

   B. angry

   C. worried

   D. excited

Explore *The Bears on Hemlock Mountain* (A)

Reading Questions

Choose the answer.

1. The words *drip, drip, drip* and *tick-tock, tick-tock* are examples of what kind of language?
   - **A.** simile
   - **B.** rhyme
   - **C.** metaphor
   - **D.** onomatopoeia

2. Which clue tells that this story takes place a long time ago?
   - **A.** Jonathan's mother does not have a telephone to call Aunt Emma and tell her that Jonathan is coming.
   - **B.** Aunt Emma has a brass knocker, a rocking chair, and a ticking clock at her house.
   - **C.** Jonathan's mother needs to use a giant pot to cook for her large family.
   - **D.** Jonathan has to feed the birds bread crumbs instead of bird seed from a store.

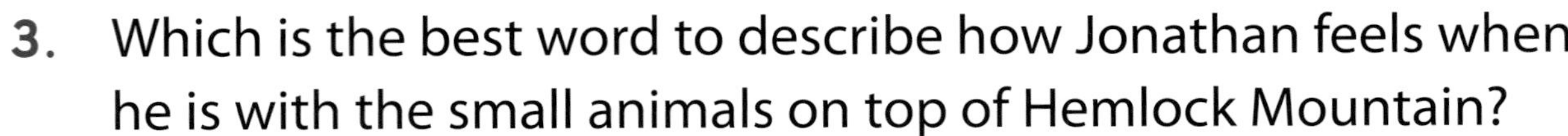

3. Which is the best word to describe how Jonathan feels when he is with the small animals on top of Hemlock Mountain?

   A. lonely

   B. afraid

   C. worried

   D. calm

4. What does Jonathan do when he gets to his aunt's house?

   A. He asks for the giant pot.

   B. He helps her feed the cat.

   C. He eats cookies and drinks milk.

   D. He talks with his aunt about the family.

5. Why does Jonathan leave his aunt's house without the pot?

   A. He is embarrassed and doesn't want to ask for it.

   B. He is in a hurry to get home because it is getting dark.

   C. He has been having a long talk with his aunt and forgets.

   D. He decides that the pot is too big for him to carry by himself.

Explore *The Bears on Hemlock Mountain* (B)

Reading Questions

Choose the answer.

1. Which words are an example of onomatopoeia?
   A. nearer and nearer and nearer
   B. sniff, sniff, sniff
   C. Hello-o-o-oh!
   D. stuff and nonsense

2. What do the bears do when they first get to the pot?
   A. They try to turn it over.
   B. They try to dig under it.
   C. They look at it and walk away.
   D. They sniff around it and then wait.

3. What helps Jonathan feel less alone as he waits under the pot?
   A. his father's voice
   B. the memory of his parents
   C. the sound of the birds in the trees
   D. the squirrels who dig under the pot

4. Why do the bears leave?
   - **A.** The other animals scare them away.
   - **B.** Jonathan makes noise and frightens them away.
   - **C.** They get bored trying to reach Jonathan under the pot.
   - **D.** They hear Jonathan's father and the other men coming.

5. What clue tells you that Jonathan's father and the other men think there might be bears on Hemlock Mountain?
   - **A.** They are carrying guns when they look for Jonathan.
   - **B.** They believe Jonathan right away when he says he has seen bears.
   - **C.** They tell Jonathan that they think there might be bears on the mountain.
   - **D.** They say they followed the bears' tracks through the snow.

Explore *The Bears on Hemlock Mountain* (B)

Choices and Consequences

Fill in the consequence of Jonathan's choice.

Jonathon's Choice		Consequence
Jonathan stops for a long time on top of the mountain.	→	
Jonathan does not tell his aunt right away why he came.	→	
Jonathan eats his aunt's cookies and drinks milk.	→	
	→	

Review *The Bears on Hemlock Mountain*

Conflict and Resolution

Fill in the resolution to the conflict.

Conflict	Resolution
Jonathan must face the dark when he leaves his aunt's house. →	
Two bears appear on the mountain. →	
The bears wait by the pot, and one starts to scrape at the snow around it. →	

Introduce "Animals in Winter!"

Reading Questions

Choose the answer.

1. What is the main idea of this article?

   A. When winter comes, some animals move to warm places, and some sleep until winter ends.

   B. Some animals enjoy winter games, but some animals do not thrive in cold weather.

   C. In the fall, when the weather gets cold, many animals build new homes.

   D. Most animals stay in their homes during the coldest winter months.

2. Which detail supports the main idea?

   A. Flocks of Canada geese fly in the shape of a big "V."

   B. Humpback whales swim to warmer waters in the winter to have their babies.

   C. Black bears like to eat berries, acorns, roots, grubs, and fish.

   D. Bats sleep upside down in caves, hollow trees, or barns.

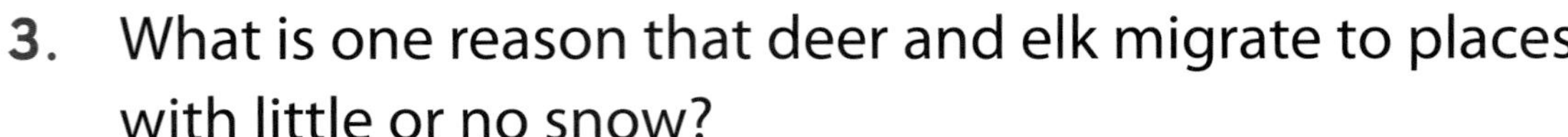

LITERATURE & COMPREHENSION

3. What is one reason that deer and elk migrate to places with little or no snow?
   - **A.** They don't like the cold temperatures in winter.
   - **B.** They need to have their babies in warmer places.
   - **C.** They need to find the grasses and other plants they eat.
   - **D.** They don't like to have snow and ice caught in their hooves.

4. Why do bats hibernate in winter?
   - **A.** There are no insects to eat in winter.
   - **B.** They don't like to fly in the cold weather.
   - **C.** They don't have fat to keep them warm.
   - **D.** All the other animals in the forest hibernate, too.

5. How are black bears and some frogs and turtles alike?
   - **A.** They migrate.
   - **B.** They hibernate.
   - **C.** They eat insects.
   - **D.** They live in the mud.

Review "Animals in Winter!"

Categorize Information

Put an X in a box when the animals fit the category.

	Migrate	Hibernate	Eat Plants	Eat Fish	Sleep in Caves
Canada geese					
deer and elk					
black bears					
frogs and turtles					
bats					
hump-back whales					

Check Your Reading

Introduce "Puss in Boots"

Reading Questions

Choose the answer.

1. Which word best describes how the miller's son feels about being left with only the cat when his father dies?
   A. excited
   B. relaxed
   C. confused
   D. disappointed

2. Why does Puss call her master the Marquis of Carabas?
   A. because that is his name
   B. so the king will be impressed
   C. because the true marquis has said it's OK
   D. so the giant will be afraid of the miller's son

3. What happens because Puss in Boots gives presents from her master to the king?
   A. The king is angry with the Marquis of Carabas.
   B. The king thinks the Marquis of Carabas is funny.
   C. The king is pleased with the Marquis of Carabas.
   D. The king thinks the Marquis of Carabas is stealing.

LITERATURE & COMPREHENSION

4. How does Puss make the king believe the land belongs to the miller's son?

   A. She tells people in the fields to say the land belongs to the marquis.

   B. She puts up a large sign that says, "Land belonging to the Marquis of Carabas."

   C. She tells the miller's son to say the land is his when the king passes by.

   D. She tells the king that the land belongs to the Marquis of Carabas.

5. Which word best describes Puss in Boots when she tricks the giant?

   A. mean

   B. clever

   C. strong

   D. fearful

Explore "Puss in Boots"

Make Inferences

Answer the questions.

1. Why does Puss give gifts to the king?

____

2. Why does Puss have her master pretend to drown so the king can save him?

____

3. Why does Puss have the workers in the field tell the king the land belongs to the marquis?

____

4. Why does Puss want the giant's castle?

____

5. At the end of the story, what does the king think of the miller's son?

____

6. Do you think Puss planned for all these things to happen? Why or why not?

____

Review "Puss in Boots"

Puss's Character Trait

Answer the questions.

1. What words describe Puss in Boots?

2. What is Puss's most important character trait?

3. Give examples from the story that support your idea about Puss's character.

4. How does this character trait help Puss and the miller's son?

LITERATURE & COMPREHENSION

Check Your Reading

Introduce "Tug-of-War"

Reading Questions

Choose the answer.

1. Why does Turtle decide to trick Elephant and Hippopotamus?
   A. He doesn't like them and wants to make them feel silly.
   B. He is repaying them for a trick they played on him.
   C. He wants them to think he is their equal.
   D. He thinks they will enjoy a good joke.

2. Which word best describes Turtle when he says he is equal to Elephant and Hippopotamus?
   A. angry
   B. boastful
   C. unhappy
   D. frustrated

3. What is the most likely reason that Elephant agrees to a tug-of-war with Turtle?
   A. He thinks he would beat Turtle easily and prove that he is stronger.
   B. He thinks that Turtle will beat him, and he doesn't mind.
   C. He wants to be nice to Turtle and play a game with him.
   D. He doesn't think that Turtle will actually play the game.

LITERATURE & COMPREHENSION

4. What does Turtle do to make sure that Elephant and Hippopotamus do **not** see each other on the ends of the vine?

   A. He tells them to look away when they begin to pull.

   B. He uses a long vine so the animals can't see each other.

   C. He puts blindfolds on them so they can't see who is pulling.

   D. He brings the vine over a hill so they can't see each other.

5. Why do Hippopotamus and Elephant call Turtle "friend" at the end of the story?

   A. They feel bad that they were mean to Turtle earlier.

   B. They want to be friendly with everyone in the jungle.

   C. They realize that someone does not have to be strong to be equal.

   D. They think that Turtle is strong and deserves to be their equal.

Explore "Tug-of-War"

Turtle's Character Trait

Complete the chart for Turtle's trait. Write the answers in the circles.

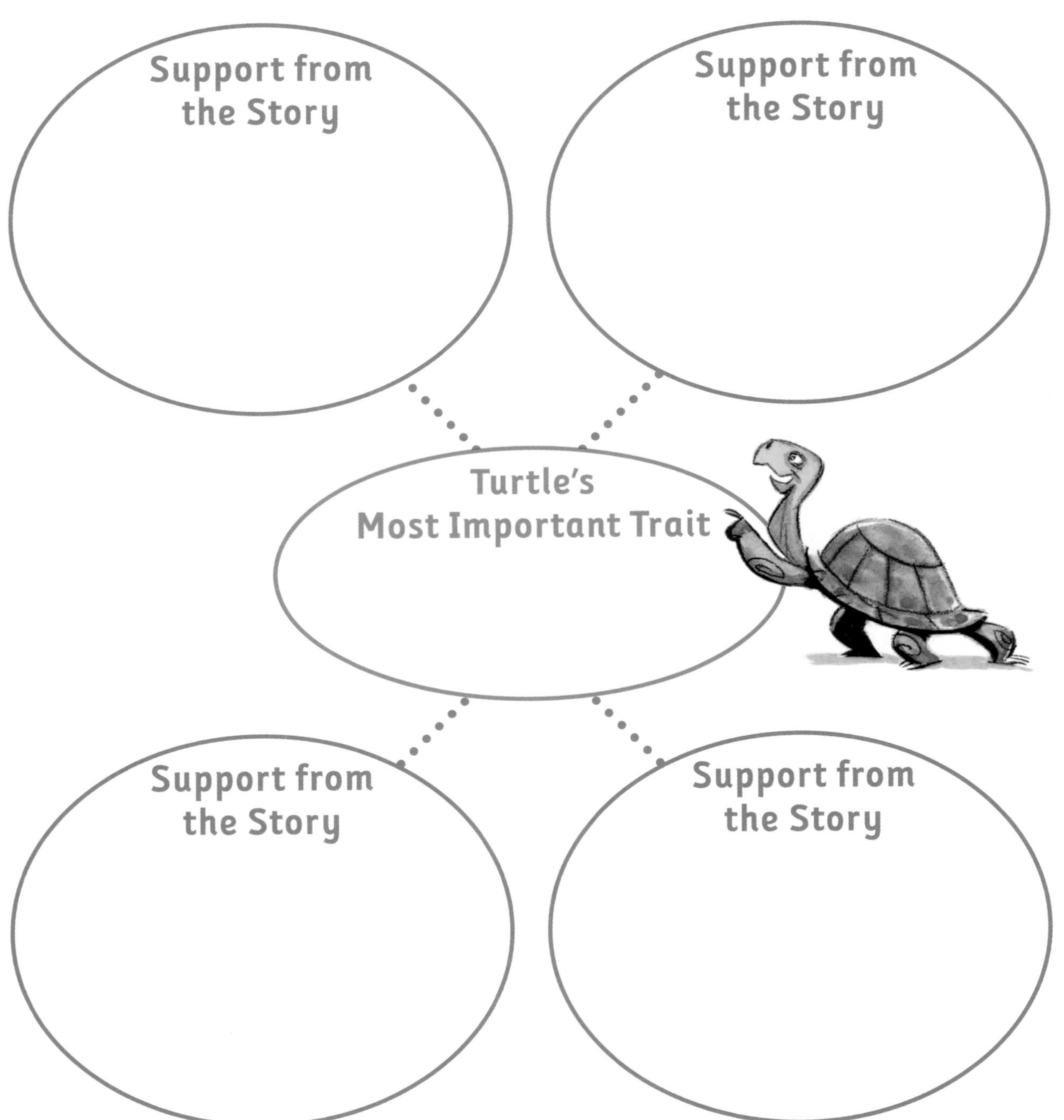

Introduce "Each Animal in Its Place"

Reading Questions

Choose the answer.

1. What is the topic of the article?
   - **A.** animals in cold places
   - **B.** animals in warm places
   - **C.** animal adaptations
   - **D.** animals and their prey

2. Where do toucans live?
   - **A.** at the North Pole
   - **B.** in the Sahara
   - **C.** near the Atlantic Ocean
   - **D.** in rain forests

3. Which of the following is an adaptation of the camel?
   - **A.** It has small hooves for walking in the sand.
   - **B.** It doesn't sweat, so it doesn't need much water.
   - **C.** It has no eyelashes, so sand doesn't get caught in them.
   - **D.** It doesn't breathe through its nose, so sand doesn't come in.

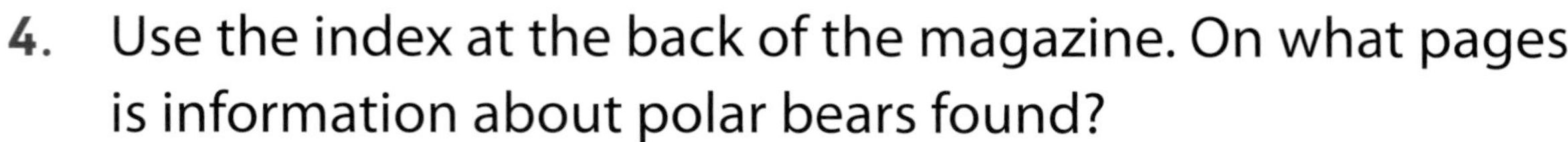

4. Use the index at the back of the magazine. On what pages is information about polar bears found?

   A. pages 20–21, 32–33, 42–43, 49

   B. pages 7–10, 32–33, 42–43

   C. pages 20–21, 32–33

   D. pages 15–17, 22–33, 40–41, 45

5. Look back at the first two pages of the article. Which word helps to know what **adaptations** means?

   A. tough

   B. features

   C. places

   D. special

Reading for Meaning

Introduce "Each Animal in Its Place"

Organize Information

Complete the chart with information about three animals from the article.

Animal	Adaptation	Reason for Adaptation

LITERATURE & COMPREHENSION

Reading for Meaning

Review "Each Animal in Its Place"

Main Idea and Supporting Details

Complete the chart with the main idea and supporting details from the article.

Main idea

Supporting Details

LITERATURE & COMPREHENSION

Check Your Reading

Introduce "The Fisherman and His Wife"

Reading Questions

LITERATURE & COMPREHENSION

Choose the answer.

1. What does the fisherman first do with the talking fish?
   - **A.** He takes it home to eat.
   - **B.** He asks for his first wish.
   - **C.** He tells his friends about it.
   - **D.** He throws it back into the sea.

2. What does the fisherman's wife do when she hears about the fish?
   - **A.** She gets angry because there won't be any dinner.
   - **B.** She tells the fisherman to go back and ask for a cottage.
   - **C.** She tells the fisherman that she doesn't believe he found a talking fish.
   - **D.** She says she is afraid the fish will harm them.

3. How does the wife feel each time the fish grants her wish?
   - **A.** She is happy for a short time, but then she wants more.
   - **B.** She is unhappy right away and immediately asks for more.
   - **C.** She is sad because she sees that the fisherman is unhappy.
   - **D.** She is surprised that her wish has come true.

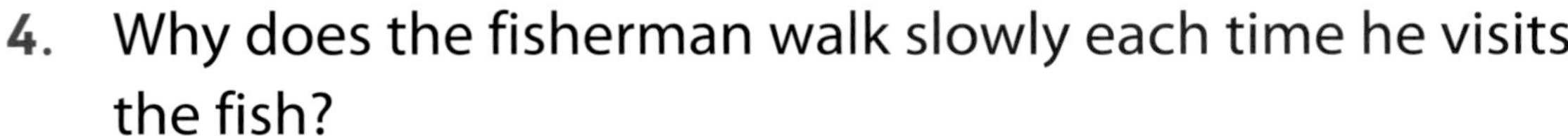

4. Why does the fisherman walk slowly each time he visits the fish?

   A. He is tired of making the long journey down to the sea.

   B. He is afraid that the fish will not grant his wife's wishes.

   C. He is sad that his wife cannot be happy.

   D. He is bored with going to see the fish time after time.

5. Why does the fish return the fisherman and his wife to their old hut in the end?

   A. The fisherman and his wife were worried that their neighbors were getting jealous.

   B. The wife asked for too much when she wanted to control the moon and sun.

   C. The fisherman and his wife had not helped anyone else with their wishes.

   D. The fisherman and his wife wanted to go back to their old life.

Reading for Meaning

Introduce "The Fisherman and His Wife"

Understand Imagery

Complete the chart using examples from the story and your own drawings.

The Wife's Wish	Description of the Sky and Sea	My Picture of the Sky and Sea
a big stone castle (page 91)		
to be queen of all the land (page 94)		
the power to make the moon and sun rise and set (page 95)		

LITERATURE & COMPREHENSION

Explore "The Fisherman and His Wife"

Describe the Characters

Answer the questions.

1. At the beginning of the story, how does the fisherman feel about his life? Support your answer with an example from the story.

   ____

   ____

2. Why is the fisherman sad when his wife wishes for things?

   ____

   ____

   ____

3. Is the wife content, or happy, with what she has in life? Give an example from the story to support your answer.

   ____

4. List two words that describe the fisherman and two words that describe the wife.

   ____

Review "The Fisherman and His Wife"

Teach the Moral

Write your own story. Then, state the moral of the story. You may illustrate your story if you wish.

1. Write your own story that teaches the moral of "The Fisherman and His Wife."

____

____

____

____

____

____

____

____

2. The moral of the story is

____

____.

Introduce "The Warrior and the Baby"

Reading Questions

Choose the answer.

1. Which word best describes the warrior?
   - **A.** kind
   - **B.** afraid
   - **C.** smart
   - **D.** proud

2. Why does Old Grandmother say there is someone mightier than the warrior?
   - **A.** She wants to challenge the warrior to a battle.
   - **B.** She knows another warrior who is braver.
   - **C.** She wants to teach the warrior a lesson.
   - **D.** She thinks her baby is better than the warrior.

3. What is the most likely reason that the baby does **not** come when the warrior calls him?
   - **A.** The baby doesn't understand the warrior.
   - **B.** The baby wants to make the warrior angry.
   - **C.** The baby has been told to stay where he is.
   - **D.** The baby is busy and doesn't hear the warrior.

4. What does Old Grandmother mean when she says "all obey" the baby?

   A. One day the baby will be chief of the village.

   B. Everyone wants to keep the baby happy.

   C. The villagers know that the baby will be a warrior one day.

   D. Everyone believes that the baby is wise and knows a lot.

5. How does the warrior feel when the baby refuses to obey him?

   A. sad

   B. frustrated

   C. excited

   D. happy

Introduce "The Warrior and the Baby"

My Summary of the Story

Write a summary of "The Warrior and the Baby."

Explore "The Warrior and the Baby"

Describe the Characters

Answer the questions.

1. What words would you use to describe the warrior?

   ___

2. Name a trait of the warrior. Give two examples of this trait from the story.

   ___

   ___

   ___

3. Choose a trait to describe Old Grandmother. Give two examples from the story as support.

   ___

   ___

Review "The Warrior and the Baby"

The Moral of the Story

Complete the sentence. Draw pictures that show how the warrior felt before and after he met the baby.

1. The moral of the story is

____

____.

2. Draw a picture of the warrior before he meets the baby.

3. Draw a picture of the warrior after he meets the baby.

Check Your Reading

Introduce Nighttime Poems

Reading Questions

Choose the answer.

1. In the poem "In the Night," what is the speaker trying to do?
   - **A.** remember a favorite song by humming it
   - **B.** get some exercise while lying in bed
   - **C.** fall back to sleep after waking up at night
   - **D.** describe how to practice singing a song

2. Why does the poet repeat the word *hum* in the poem "In the Night"?
   - **A.** She wants the reader to repeat the word.
   - **B.** She wants the poem to sound like humming.
   - **C.** She can't think of any other word to use.
   - **D.** She thinks the word is fun to say.

3. Why is the speaker glad to have a Teddy-bear in the poem "Night Bear"?
   - **A.** The Teddy-bear makes her feel safe and cozy.
   - **B.** The Teddy-bear is like a pet the speaker wants to have.
   - **C.** The Teddy-bear reminds the speaker of bears in the zoo.
   - **D.** The Teddy-bear is more comfortable than a pillow.

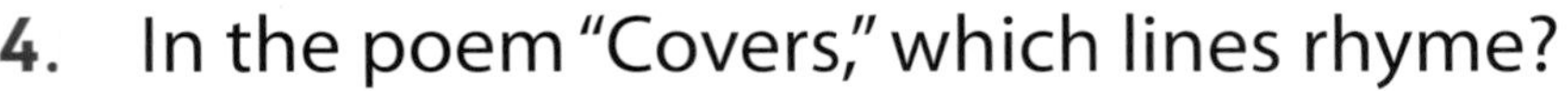

LITERATURE & COMPREHENSION

4. In the poem "Covers," which lines rhyme?

   A. lines 1 and 2

   B. lines 1 and 3

   C. lines 2 and 2

   D. lines 2 and 4

5. Who is the speaker talking to in the poem "De Koven"?

   A. a neighbor

   B. a boy

   C. a star

   D. the reader

Introduce Nighttime Poems

What Does "Covers" Mean?

Write the names of the types of covers the poet describes in "Covers." Then, write other meanings of the word *covers*.

Type of cover:	Type of cover:	Other meanings:
Type of cover:	Other meanings:	Other meanings:
Type of cover:	Other meanings:	Other meanings:

Reread the end of the poem. How is nighttime like a cover?

____

Introduce "Bedtime" and "Sun for Breakfast"

Reading Questions

Choose the answer.

1. Which words rhyme in the poem "Bedtime?"
   A. jump, away, creep
   B. hop, skip, night
   C. night, day, coaxes
   D. leap, creep, sleep

2. In "Bedtime," what does *Night comes and coaxes / The world to sleep* mean?
   A. At night, people are tired.
   B. It gets dark at nighttime.
   C. There are no sounds at night
   D. Nighttime is very creepy.

3. What is the main idea of "Sun for Breakfast"?
   A. Every day is sunny.
   B. Every day is a new beginning.
   C. People should be able to eat sunshine.
   D. The morning is the best time of day.

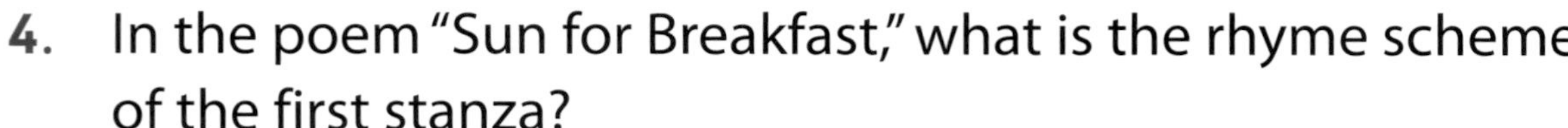

4. In the poem "Sun for Breakfast," what is the rhyme scheme of the first stanza?

   A. The rhyme sceme is AB.

   B. The rhyme sceme is AA.

   C. The rhyme sceme is BB.

   D. The rhyme sceme is BC.

5. What is the main idea of "Sun for Breakfast"?

   A. People are hungry when they wake up in the morning, so they should eat breakfast.

   B. People who wake up hungry in the morning should take a walk or a shower first.

   C. People should be excited about a new day and should wake up and get going.

   D. People should take whatever they need in the world and not worry about others.

Introduce "Bedtime" and "Sun for Breakfast"

Personification

Write a line from "Bedtime" or "Sun for Breakfast" that shows personification. Then, draw a picture to illustrate the line.

1. Line from "Bedtime" or "Sun for Breakfast" that shows personification:

   ____

   ____

2. Draw a picture that shows what you think this image looks like.

Introduce "Bed in Summer"

Reading Questions

Choose the answer.

1. Which line from the poem tells that the speaker is a child?
   - **A.** In winter I get up at night
   - **B.** I have to go to bed by day.
   - **C.** Or hear the grown-up people's feet
   - **D.** And does it not seem hard to you,

2. When the speaker gets up in the winter it is ______________.
   - **A.** dark
   - **B.** light
   - **C.** raining
   - **D.** hot

3. Which does **not** happen when the speaker goes to bed in summer?
   - **A.** The birds hop in the trees.
   - **B.** It is dark outside.
   - **C.** The people walk by on the street.
   - **D.** The sky is blue.

4. What happens as the speaker goes to bed in summer?
   - **A.** People get dressed in the dark.
   - **B.** People light candles.
   - **C.** People pull down their window shades.
   - **D.** People walk in the streets and birds sing.

5. How does the speaker feel about going to bed in summer?
   - **A.** thankful
   - **B.** peaceful
   - **C.** frustrated
   - **D.** worried

Introduce "Bed in Summer"

Rhyme Scheme

Write the rhyme scheme of the poem.

Bed in Summer

by Robert Louis Stevenson

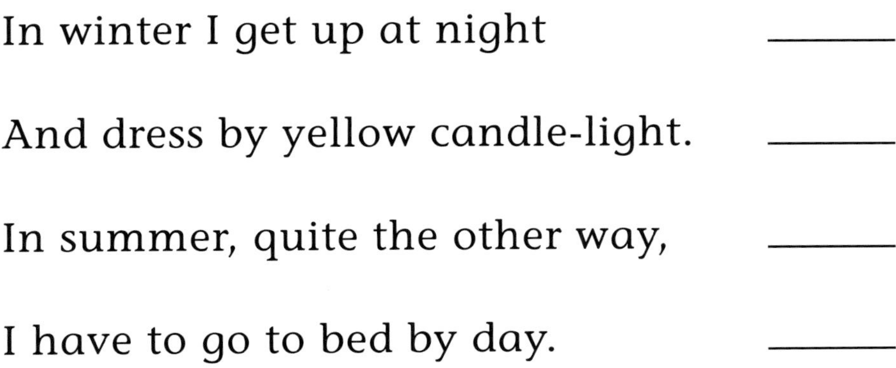

In winter I get up at night ______
And dress by yellow candle-light. ______
In summer, quite the other way, ______
I have to go to bed by day. ______

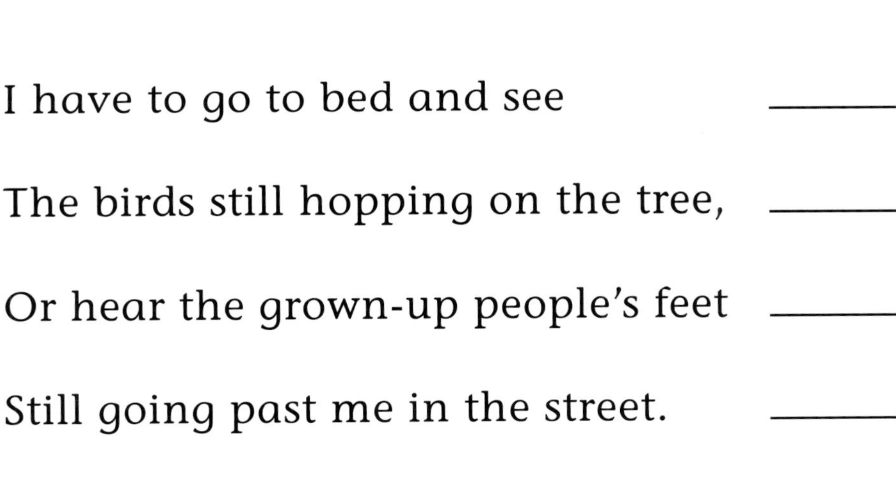

I have to go to bed and see ______
The birds still hopping on the tree, ______
Or hear the grown-up people's feet ______
Still going past me in the street. ______

And does it not seem hard to you, ______
When all the sky is clear and blue, ______
And I should like so much to play, ______
To have to go to bed by day? ______

Introduce "Rumpelstiltskin"

Reading Questions

Choose the answer.

1. Why does the miler say his daughter can spin straw into gold?
   - **A.** She really can make gold.
   - **B.** He wants to impress the king.
   - **C.** He knows the king needs more gold.
   - **D.** He wants his daughter to get a job in the palace.

2. What does the king say will happen if the girl does **not** spin straw into gold in one night?
   - **A.** He will give her another night to try.
   - **B.** He will get a magical elf to help her.
   - **C.** He will put her to death in the morning.
   - **D.** He will find her other work to do in the palace.

3. Why does Rumpelstiltskin help the girl?
   - **A.** He wants payment from her.
   - **B.** He is a kind and helpful elf.
   - **C.** He has promised the king he will help her.
   - **D.** He hopes that she will marry him.

LITERATURE & COMPREHENSION

4. Why does Rumpelstiltskin say he will **not** take the child if the queen can guess his name?
   - **A.** He does not really want her child.
   - **B.** He does not think the queen will guess.
   - **C.** The king has told him to test the queen.
   - **D.** The miller has told him the queen likes riddles.

5. How does the queen find out Rumpelstiltskin's name?
   - **A.** A fairy tells her his name.
   - **B.** The king tells her his name.
   - **C.** She overhears him say it.
   - **D.** Her page overhears him say it.

Reading for Meaning

Introduce "Rumpelstiltskin"

Characters in "Rumpelstiltskin"

First, write an adjective for the character. Then, complete the sentence with information from the story about what the character says or does, or what others say about the character.

LITERATURE & COMPREHENSION

1. The miller is ______________________________ because ______________________________.

2. The king is ______________________________ because ______________________________.

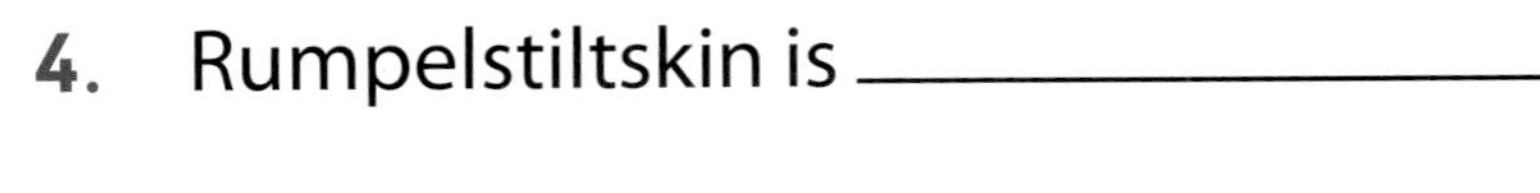

3. The girl is ______________________________ because ______________________________.

4. Rumpelstiltskin is ______________________________

because ______________________________

______________________________.

Explore "Rumpelstiltskin"

Problems and Solutions

LITERATURE & COMPREHENSION

Match the problem with its solution.

Problems	Solutions
The miller's daughter must spin gold the first time.	The miller's daughter gives Rumpelstiltskin her necklace.
The miller's daughter must spin gold the second time.	The queen tells Rumpelstiltskin his name and keeps her baby.
The miller's daughter must spin gold the third time.	The queen must find out Rumpelstiltskin's name.
Rumpelstiltskin comes to take the queen's baby.	The miller's daugther gives Rumpelstiltskin her ring.
The queen does not know Rumpelstiltskin's name.	A page overhears Rumpelstiltskin singing his name and tells the queen.
Rumpelstiltskin comes back to find out if the queen knows his name.	The miller's daughter agrees to give Rumpelstiltskin her first child.

Introduce "The Hippopotamus and the Tortoise"

Reading Questions

Choose the answer.

1. What is the hippopotamus the big king of?
   - **A.** the water
   - **B.** the jungle
   - **C.** the land
   - **D.** the forest

2. What does the hippopotamus like to do for his friends?
   - **A.** give them gifts
   - **B.** give them big feasts
   - **C.** give them riddles to solve
   - **D.** give them parts of his kingdom

3. What does the hippopotamus promise if the tortoise finds out his name?
   - **A.** He will stop giving big feasts forever.
   - **B.** He will make everyone leave his next feast.
   - **C.** He will be ashamed and hide his face forever.
   - **D.** He will leave the land forever and live in the water.

4. What does the tortoise do to learn the hippo's name?
   - A. He asks all the other animals if they know it.
   - B. He hides and waits for the hippo to say his name.
   - C. He tells names to the hippo until he gets the right one.
   - D. He trips the hippo's sister so that he can hear her say the name.

5. Which of the following words best describes the tortoise?
   - A. bossy
   - B. clever
   - C. afraid
   - D. angry

Introduce "The Hippopotamus and the Tortoise"

Story Cube

Complete the sentences. Cut out the shape and fold along the lines. Glue or tape the tabs.

Setting: The story takes place in a land

Character: One of the main characters is

Character: One of the main characters is

Problem: Tortoise needs to learn the

Solution: Tortoise solves his problem by

Conclusion: Hippo must

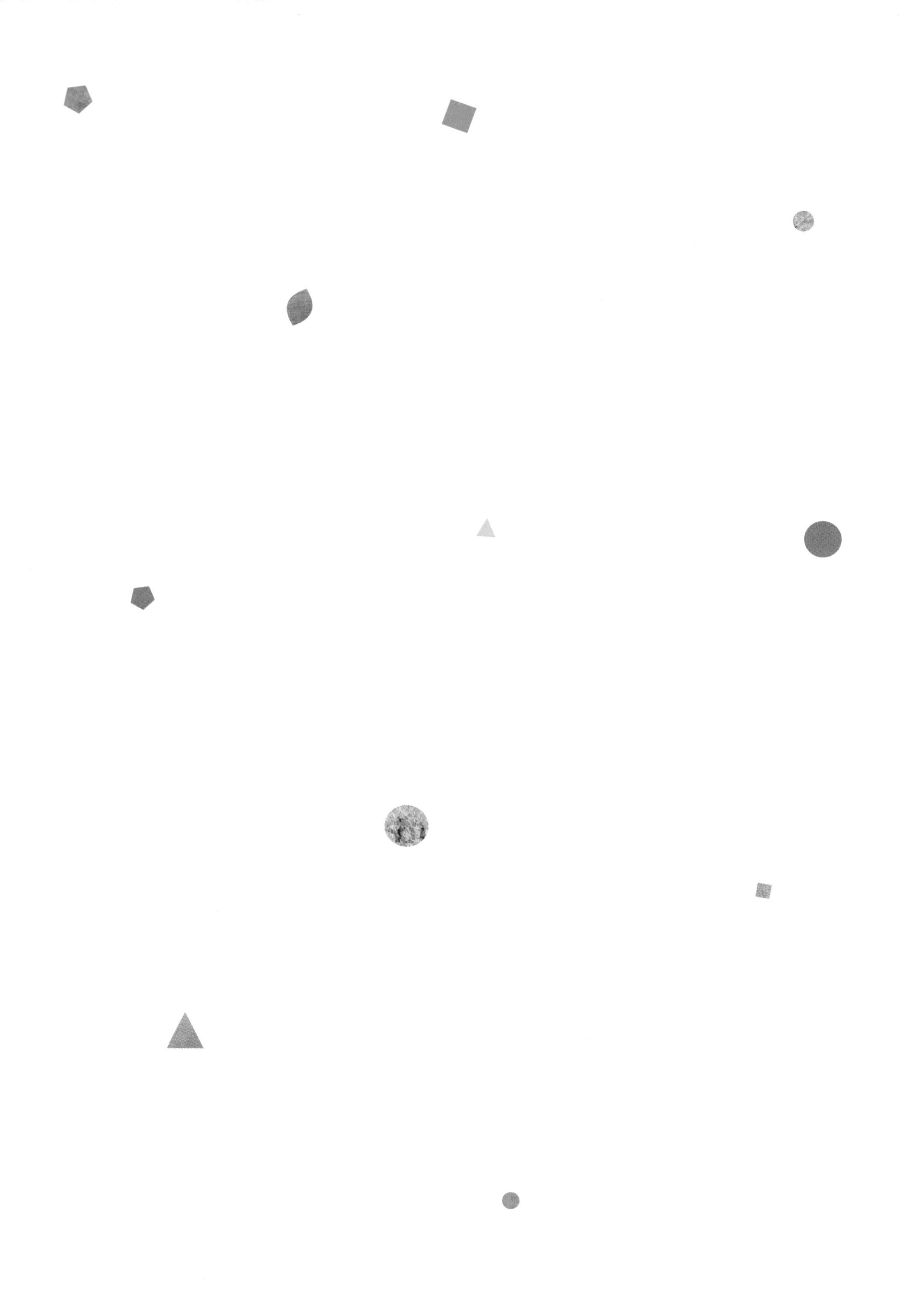

Review "The Hippopotamus and the Tortoise"

Compare and Contrast Folktales

Answer the questions about "The Hippopotamus and the Tortoise," "The Jackals and the Lion," and "Tug-of-War."

1. In these three tales, who are the smaller, weaker characters?

___

2. In these three tales, who are the larger, stronger characters?

___

___

3. Which characters are successful in these tales, the smaller ones or the larger ones? Why are they successful?

___

4. Before you read the stories, who would you have predicted would have been more successful? Why?

___

___

5. What do these tales tell you was important to the people who told them?

___

Introduce Weather Poems

Reading Questions

Choose the answer.

1. What is the rhyme scheme of the first stanza in the poem "Sudden Storm"?
   A. The rhyme scheme is ABCD.
   B. The rhyme scheme is ABAB.
   C. The rhyme scheme is ABAC.
   D. The rhyme scheme is AABB.

2. Why does the poet compare umbrellas to mushrooms and flowers in the poem "Sudden Storm"?
   A. All are useful in the rain.
   B. All are round and colorful.
   C. All come out when it rains.
   D. None of them likes to get wet.

3. In the poem "Never Mind the Rain," which phrase is repeated?
   A. rain and snow
   B. Never mind
   C. before you know
   D. It melts

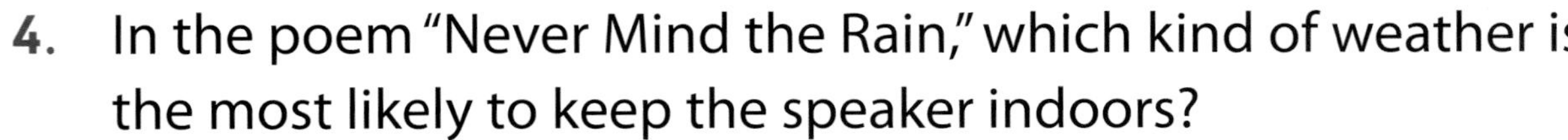

4. In the poem "Never Mind the Rain," which kind of weather is the most likely to keep the speaker indoors?
   - **A.** cold and rainy
   - **B.** snowy and cloudy
   - **C.** rainy and windy
   - **D.** rainy and snowy

5. What is the rhyme scheme of the poem "First Snow"?
   - **A.** The rhyme scheme is AABB.
   - **B.** The rhyme scheme is ABAB.
   - **C.** The rhyme scheme is ABCB.
   - **D.** The rhyme scheme is ABCD.

6. In the poem "First Snow," why does the speaker say that the places where she plays "Look like somewhere else today"?
   - **A.** They were moved overnight.
   - **B.** They have been covered with snow.
   - **C.** She's dreaming and they look different.
   - **D.** They remind her of other places she knows.

Introduce Weather Poems

Simile and Metaphor

Use the poem "First Snow" to answer the questions.

1. Find and write the simile in the poem.

2. What two things are being compared in the simile?

3. How are these two things alike?

4. What else could you compare to snow that is different from snow but also like it in some way? Think about how snow looks and feels.

5. Write a metaphor for snow using your idea about how snow looks and feels.

Check Your Reading

Introduce More Weather Poems

Reading Questions

Choose the answer.

1. In the poem "In August," which two words in the first stanza rhyme?
   - **A.** *hot* and *trot*
   - **B.** *strong* and *around*
   - **C.** *clothes* and *ourselves*
   - **D.** *strong* and *hose*

2. In the poem "Change in the Weather," why does the speaker want snow and sleet in summer?
   - **A.** It's her favorite weather.
   - **B.** She likes to wear winter clothes.
   - **C.** The beaches would be less crowded.
   - **D.** It would feel good in the summer heat.

3. In the poem "Sun After Rain," what kind of weather does the poem describe?
   - **A.** snowy
   - **B.** sunny
   - **C.** cloudy
   - **D.** rainy

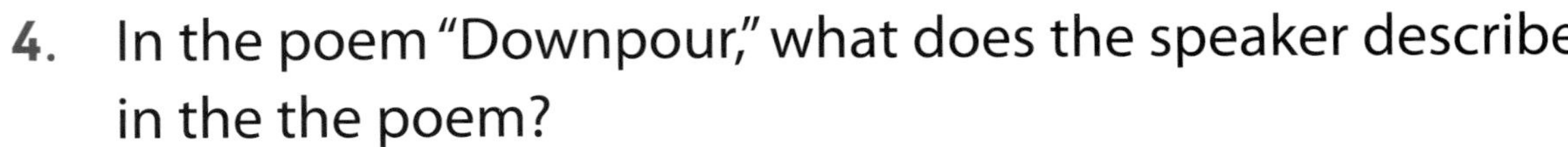

4. In the poem "Downpour," what does the speaker describe in the the poem?
   - **A.** the weather outside
   - **B.** a game to play in the rain
   - **C.** clothes to wear in the rain
   - **D.** things to do when it's raining

5. In the poem "Downpour," what is surprising about the speaker in the last line?
   - **A.** The speaker is hurrying outside.
   - **B.** The speaker is watching the rain.
   - **C.** The speaker is inside, not outside.
   - **D.** The speaker is happy that it's raining.

Introduce More Weather Poems

Personification

Use the poem "Sun After Rain" to answer the questions.

1. In the poem, what is **not** human but does some human things?

 ____

2. Describe the human act.

 ____

3. What picture does the poem's language help you see in your mind?

 ____

 ____

 ____

Introduce *The Long Way Westward*

Reading Questions

Choose the answer.

1. Which word best describes Carl Erik, Jonas, and their family?
   - **A.** cruel
   - **B.** brave
   - **C.** angry
   - **D.** powerful

2. Why does the family move to America?
   - **A.** They like traveling to new and exciting places.
   - **B.** They want to visit the family who has moved from Sweden.
   - **C.** They want to see America's gold streets for themselves.
   - **D.** They hope to make a better life in America.

3. Mamma says that New York is a crowded and noisy city, and she is glad the family isn't staying there. Which is most likely true?
   - **A.** The family comes from a quiet village or country place in Sweden.
   - **B.** The family has never been to a city before.
   - **C.** Mamma knows their new home is going to be a big house.
   - **D.** Mamma is afraid of new people.

4. Which detail from the story is most likely a fact?

   A. Jonas thinks there is a king's train in America.

   B. Jonas and Carl Erik sleep on the floor of the train.

   C. There is an emigrant train to take the family to Philadelphia.

   D. The family is headed for Minnesota.

5. What do the boys learn from their first train ride?

   A. Not everyone in America is treated the same way.

   B. All Americans are nice to strangers they meet.

   C. The trains will get them to Minnesota quickly.

   D. There are only old, uncomfortable trains to Philadelphia.

Explore *The Long Way Westward* (A)

Reading Questions

Choose the answer.

1. Across what state do the Swedish immigrants travel in Chapter 2?
   - **A.** New York
   - **B.** Ohio
   - **C.** Pennsylvania
   - **D.** Sweden

2. Which words best describe how Jonas's family feels about the land they see outside the trains?
   - **A.** excited and hopeful
   - **B.** bored and angry
   - **C.** confused and worried
   - **D.** frustrated and jealous

LITERATURE & COMPREHENSION

3. What is the difference between the Swedish women's work and the men's work?
   - **A.** The women work at night and the men work in the day.
   - **B.** The women take their work with them and the men work only on their farms.
   - **C.** The women get help from the children, but the men do their work on their own.
   - **D.** The women's work is easy and quick, but the men's work is hard and takes longer.

4. In the picture on pages 40 and 41, where are the immigrants sleeping?
   - **A.** in a field at a farm
   - **B.** in someone's house
   - **C.** outside a store in Pittsburgh
   - **D.** inside the Pittsburgh train station

5. What do the immigrants think will happen in America?
   - **A.** They will make more money and have a better life.
   - **B.** They will have a better king who will make life easier.
   - **C.** The land and climate will be worse, but they will not need to farm.
   - **D.** There won't be any other Swedes, but they will make a community with new people.

Explore *The Long Way Westward* (A)

Compare and Contrast Sweden and America

Fill in the Venn diagram with differences and similarities between Sweden and America. Find examples from Chapters 1 and 2.

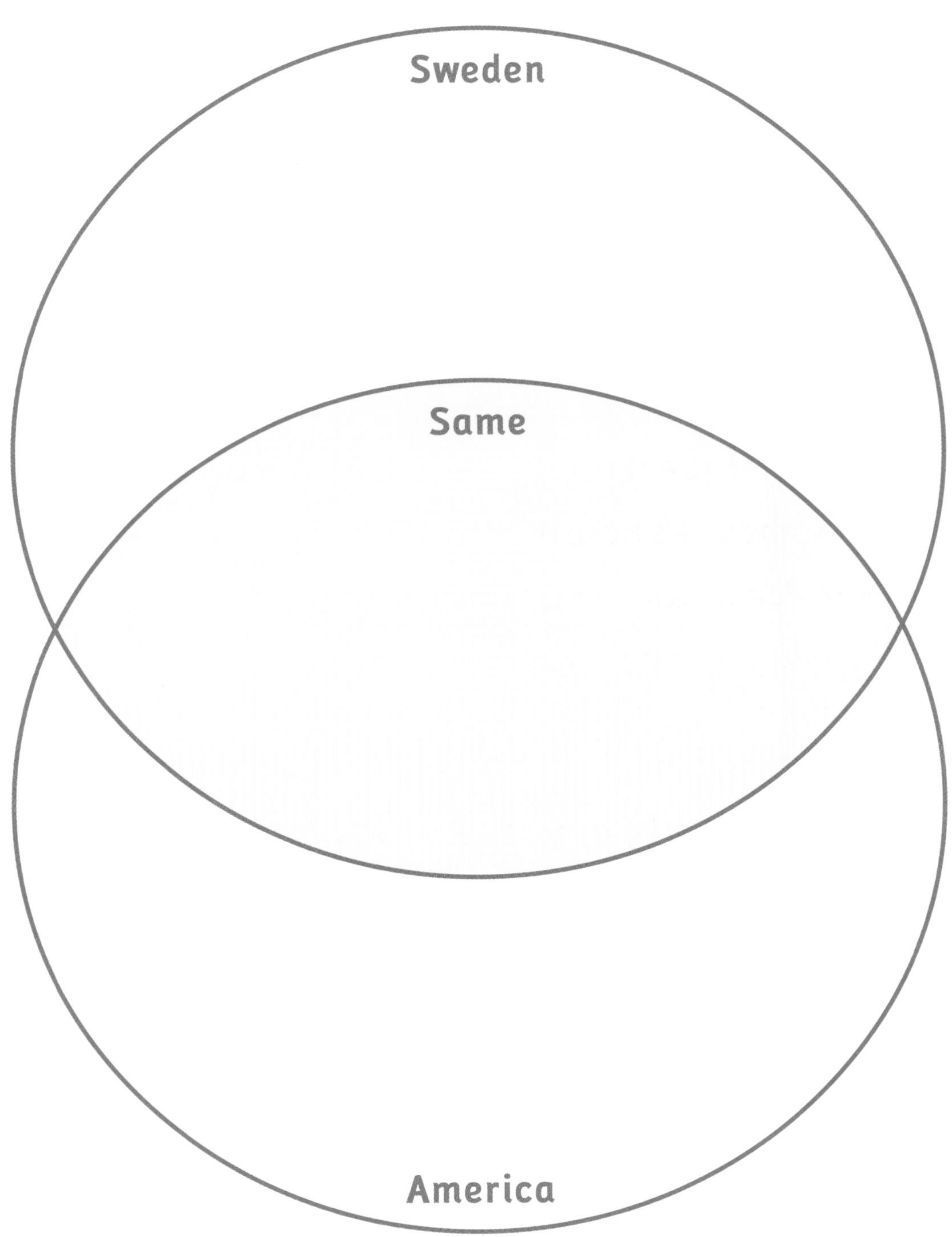

Explore *The Long Way Westward* (B)

Reading Questions

Choose the answer.

1. Why does the runner tell Mamma there are no more trains?
   - **A.** He wants to help the family find food.
   - **B.** He wants to rob the family of their belongings.
   - **C.** He wants to fool the family into staying in Chicago.
   - **D.** He wants to show the family where they can stay.

2. How does Big Carlson help Jonas's family?
   - **A.** He tells them where to sleep for the night.
   - **B.** He teaches them some English words.
   - **C.** He helps them find their next train.
   - **D.** He buys them food for dinner.

3. Who travels in the first-class cabins on the steamboat?
   - **A.** immigrants
   - **B.** wealthy people
   - **C.** poor people
   - **D.** rude people

LITERATURE & COMPREHENSION

4. Which clue tells that Carl Erik is speaking in English when he asks for directions in St. Paul?
   A. Carl Erik's question is written in English.
   B. The narrator says that Carl Erik asked in English.
   C. Carl Erik's question is written inside quotation marks.
   D. He uses a handbook, and the man answers in Swedish.

5. Which word best describes how Mamma feels to be in Anoka?
   A. content
   B. nervous
   C. terrified
   D. stressed

Explore *The Long Way Westward* (B)

A Letter from Jonas to a Friend

Imagine that you are Jonas. Write a letter to a friend back in Sweden. Tell your friend about what you see and how you feel in America.

10 Swedes Way
Anoka, Minnesota
October 10, 1868

Dear Sven,

____

____

____

____

____

____

____

Your friend,
Jonas

Explore *The Long Way Westward* (B)

Chart the Journey

Write the type of transportation the immigrants use and why it is needed. Use the story and the map to help you answer.

Part of the Trip	Type of Transportation	Why This Transportation
From Sweden to New York		
From New York to New Jersey		
From New Jersey to Philadelphia		
From Philadelphia to Pittsburgh		
From Pittsburgh to Chicago		
From Chicago to La Crosse		
Frome La Crosse to St. Paul		
From St. Paul to Anoka		

Review *The Long Way Westward*

Life in America in the 1800s

Use the book to find facts about train travelers during the late 1800s.

1. List three facts about wealthy train travelers in the late 1800s.

____

____

____

____

____

2. List three facts about poor, immigrant train travelers in the 1800s.

____

____

____

____

____

Introduce "Pioneers Go West"

Reading Questions

Choose the answer.

1. What is the main idea of the article "Pioneers Go West"?
   - A. Pioneers had a good time on their trip to the West.
   - B. Many pioneers made the difficult trip to the West along the Oregon Trail.
   - C. Pioneers who traveled west could be hurt or even killed along the way.
   - D. Pioneers used wagons to carry their belongings on the way west.

2. Which detail best supports the main idea of the article?
   - A. In 1843, the Applegates joined a wagon train to go to Oregon.
   - B. Chimney Rock was a natural landmark for pioneers.
   - C. Pioneers used buffalo chips instead of wood to make fires.
   - D. Pioneers bought supplies at forts and trading posts.

3. Why did pioneers move to the West, even though the trip was dangerous?

   A. They were forced out of their old homes.

   B. They liked adventure and taking chances.

   C. They wanted free farmland to make new homes.

   D. They were looking for jobs in factories in the West.

4. Which example shows how pioneers worked together along the Oregon Trail?

   A. They walked instead of riding in their wagons.

   B. They looked for landmarks like moutains and forts.

   C. They traded their goods with the Native Americans for food.

   D. They tied their wagons together when they crossed big rivers.

5. Why did pioneers look for landmarks?

   A. They wanted to know where Native Americans lived.

   B. They used the landmarks to tell them where they were.

   C. They wanted to leave messages at the landmarks for other pioneers.

   D. They wanted to compare their new homes with the homes they left behind.

Introduce "Pioneers Go West"

Problems and Solutions

Write each problem the pioneers faced on the trip west and how they solved it.

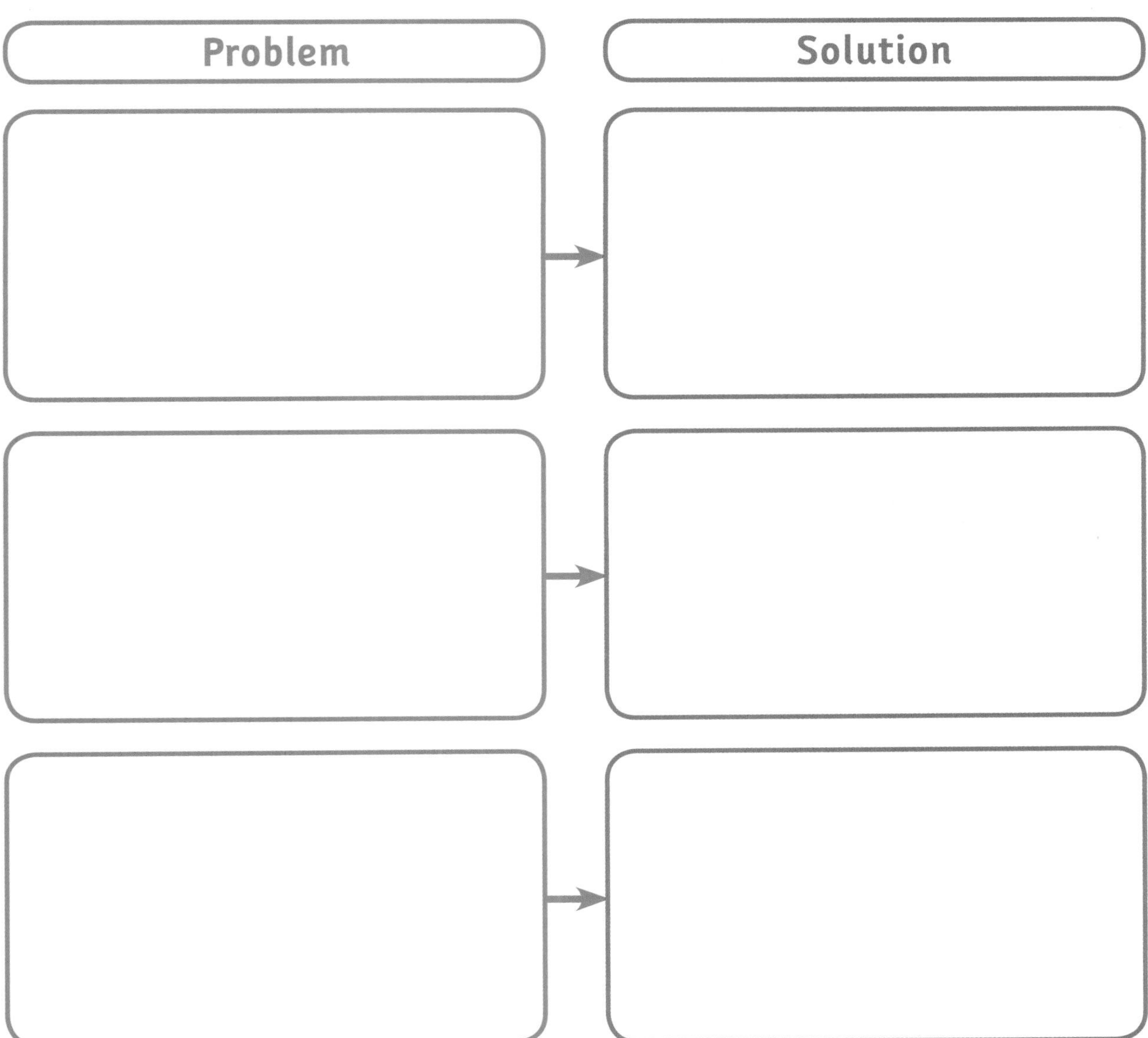

What do the pioneers' solutions tell us about them?

Reading for Meaning

Review "Pioneers Go West"

Use Visuals

Use the article, pictures, and map to answer the questions.

1. Pioneers had to cross rivers. Name one river they had to cross.

 ____

2. Why did Jesse's group tie their wagons and oxen together when crossing the river?

 ____

3. One landmark that Jesse saw was a tall rock. What was the name of the landmark?

 ____

4. How did this landmark get its name?

 ____

5. Pioneers stopped at trading posts for supplies. What is the name of the fort where the Applegates stopped?

 ____

6. Pioneers had to cross the mountains, such as the Rocky Mountains. Why was this dangerous?

 ____

Check Your Reading

Introduce "Where Go the Boats?"

Reading Questions

Choose the answer.

1. What is the rhyme scheme of the last stanza of the poem?
   - **A.** The rhyme scheme is AABB.
   - **B.** The rhyme scheme is ABCD.
   - **C.** The rhyme scheme is ABAB.
   - **D.** The rhyme scheme is ABCB.

2. In the second stanza, which word rhymes with the word *foam*?
   - **A.** *home*
   - **B.** *boats*
   - **C.** *a-floating*
   - **D.** *a-boating*

3. What is the setting of the poem?
   - **A.** in the woods
   - **B.** by the ocean
   - **C.** along the edge of a river
   - **D.** by a mill in a town

LITERATURE & COMPREHENSION

4. What does the speaker see floating on the river?
   - **A.** trees
   - **B.** leaves
   - **C.** mills
   - **D.** children

5. What does the speaker of the poem want to know?
   - **A.** what happens to boats that sail down the river
   - **B.** who else watches the river flowing
   - **C.** why there are leaves and foam in the river
   - **D.** why there is a mill along the river

Introduce "Where Go the Boats?"

Who Is the Speaker?

Use the second stanza of the poem to answer the questions.

1. Which line in the second stanza tells you the speaker is talking about himself?

   ____

2. Which word tells you the speaker is talking about himself?

   ____

Use the last stanza of the poem to answer the questions.

3. Is the speaker an adult or a child? ______________

4. Write the line that tells you this. ______________

5. Think about the speaker's age. What kind of boats does he mean when he says, "Boats of mine a-boating"?

   ____

6. Reread the poem. What is the speaker wondering about?

   ____

7. What does the speaker think will happen to his boats?

   ____

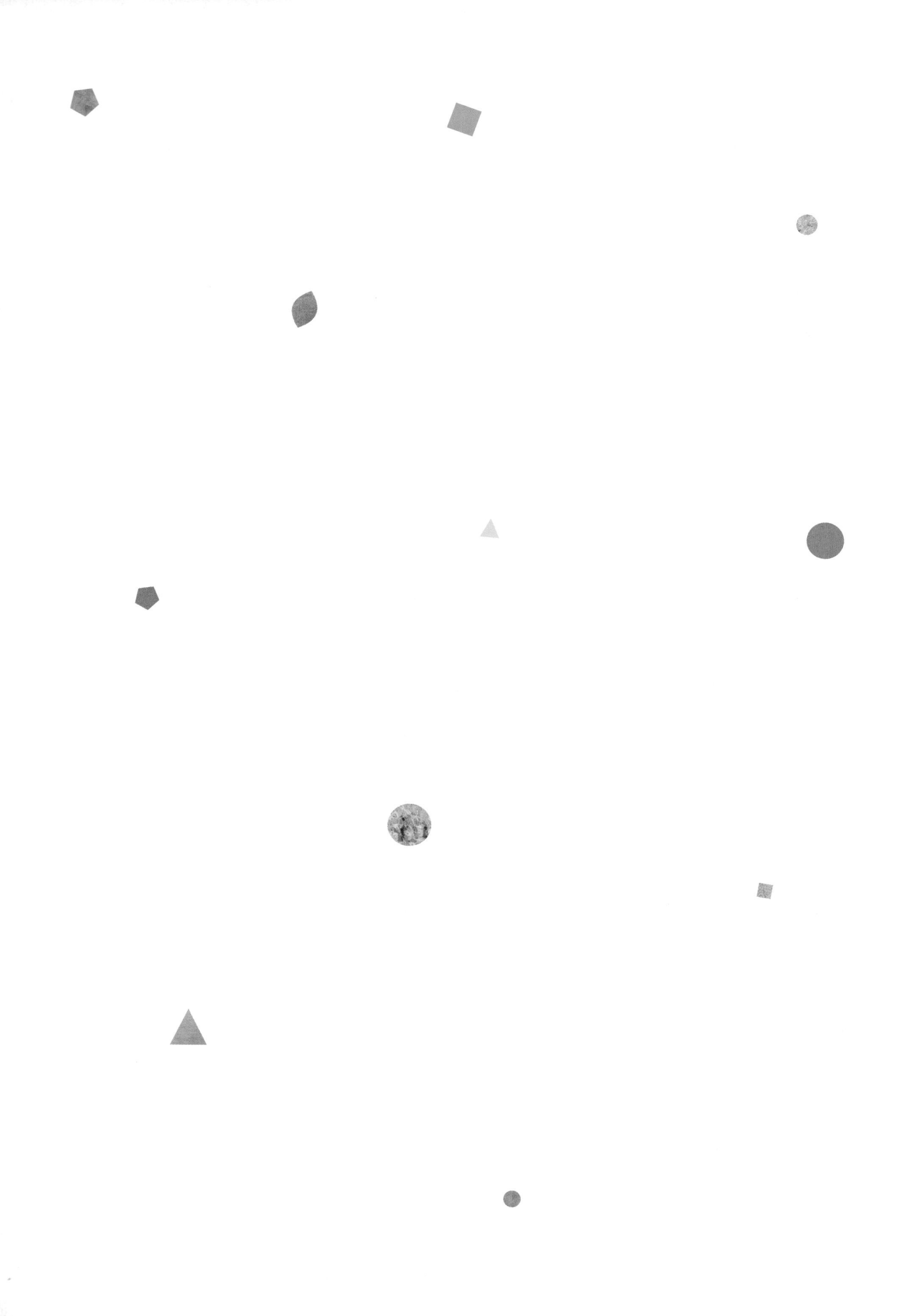

Introduce Transportation Poems

Reading Questions

Choose the answer.

1. In the poem "Taking Off," what is the meaning of "It skims above the trees"?
   - **A.** The plane bumps into the trees.
   - **B.** The plane flies just over the treetops.
   - **C.** The plane bounces over the trees.
   - **D.** The plane can be seen through the trees.

2. In the poem "Taking Off," what is the meaning of "It's just a speck against the sky"?
   - **A.** The plane looks smaller as it flies higher.
   - **B.** The plane looks small when the speaker is inside it.
   - **C.** The plane looks dirty compared to the sky.
   - **D.** The plane looks dirty next to the white clouds.

3. In the poem "Up in the Air," what does the word *blue* in the last line refer to?
   - **A.** the future
   - **B.** the ocean
   - **C.** the sky
   - **D.** sadness

4. In the poem "Up in the Air," what does the speaker want to do?

   A. watch a plane take off

   B. travel in a plane

   C. build a plane

   D. fly a plane

5. In the poem "The Subway Train," what is the rhyme scheme in the first stanza?

   A. The rhyme scheme is AABB.

   B. The rhyme scheme is ABAB.

   C. The rhyme scheme is ABCB.

   D. The rhyme scheme is ABCB.

6. In the poem "The Subway Train," why does the poet repeat the word *deep*?

   A. He likes the sound of the word.

   B. *Deep* rhymes with *beetle*.

   C. He wants to use personification.

   D. Repeating *deep* shows that the subway is far underground.

Introduce Transportation Poems

Simile

Answer the questions.

1. In "Up in the Air," what is the simile for an airplane?

____

2. In "The Subway Train," what is the simile for a subway train?

____

3. Write the name of a type of transportation other than a plane or subway.

____

4. Write words and phrases to describe the type of transportation you named in Question 3.

____

5. Write a simile for your type of transportation.

____

6. Draw a picture of your simile.

Introduce More Transportation Poems

Reading Questions

Choose the answer.

1. Which is a simile from the poem "Out for a Ride"?
   - **A.** out for a ride
   - **B.** a little puff boat
   - **C.** white as a marshmallow
   - **D.** whiffing down the river

2. Which is an example of onomatopoeia in the poem "A Peanut"?
   - **A.** all a-flutter
   - **B.** Toot toot!
   - **C.** round the bend
   - **D.** Peanut butter!

3. Which line in the poem "A Peanut" contains an example of personification?
   - **A.** Its heart was all a-flutter—
   - **B.** Choo-choo train
   - **C.** Comes round the bend,
   - **D.** Toot toot!

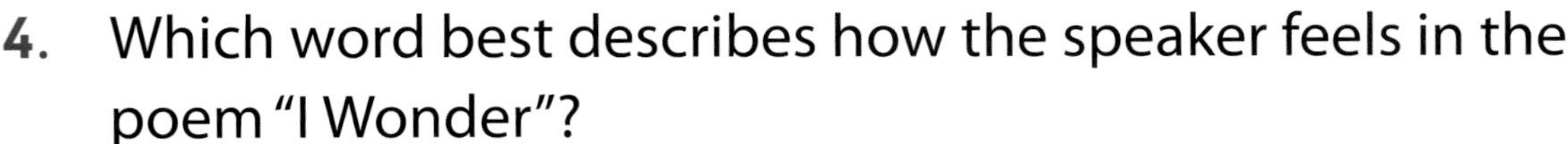

4. Which word best describes how the speaker feels in the poem "I Wonder"?
   A. unhappy
   B. angry
   C. sad
   D. curious

5. What is the rhyme scheme of the poem "Flying"?
   A. The rhyme scheme is AABBCC.
   B. The rhyme scheme is ABABA.
   C. The rhyme scheme is ABCBD.
   D. The rhyme scheme is ABBCA.

Introduce More Transportation Poems

Simile and Metaphor

Use the poem "Flying" to answer the questions.

1. In the metaphor "Over the hills of the sky you glide," what are the "hills of the sky"?

   ____

2. What two things is the poet comparing in this metaphor?

   ____

3. Why does the poet compare these two things?

   ____

4. In the metaphor "The plane is a sled for you to ride," what two things is the poet comparing?

   ____

5. What do you know about sleds?

   ____

6. Why do you think the poet compares a plane to a sled?

   ____

   ____

Introduce More Transportation Poems

The Poem I Liked Best

Answer the questions.

1. Which poem about transportation did you like best? Write the title.

   ____

2. Why did you like this poem best?

   ____

   ____

Draw a picture to illustrate this poem. Try to draw the image that was most important.

Introduce "The Dog and His Shadow"

Reading Questions

Choose the answer.

1. Where does the big dog get the bone that he has?
   - **A.** His owner gives it to him.
   - **B.** Another dog gives it to him.
   - **C.** He takes it from a little dog.
   - **D.** He finds it near a brook.

2. Why does the dog go onto the bridge?
   - **A.** He wants to look at his reflection in the brook.
   - **B.** He is thirsty and wants a drink from the brook.
   - **C.** He is running away from a dog who wants his bone.
   - **D.** He wants to bury his bone on the other side of the brook.

3. What does the big dog think he sees in the water?
   - **A.** his own reflection
   - **B.** a bone at the bottom of the brook
   - **C.** another dog with a bone
   - **D.** fish and leaves floating

4. Why does the the big dog bark at his reflection?

   A. He wants to be friendly and say hello to the dog he sees.

   B. He wants to scare the dog he sees into giving up its bone.

   C. He is scared and thinks the dog he sees might take his bone.

   D. He is curious and wants to know more about the dog he sees.

5. What does the big dog have at the end of the story?

   A. a new hiding place

   B. more friends

   C. two bones

   D. nothing

Introduce "The Dog and His Shadow"

Character Trait

Answer the questions.

1. What does the big dog do with bones?

____

____

____

2. Why does the big dog lose the bone he has?

____

____

3. Write two words you would use to describe the big dog's character.

____

____

Making Connections

Review "The Dog and His Shadow"

Compare Stories

Choose a story to compare with "The Dog and His Shadow." Then, answer the questions.

1. The moral of "The Dog and His Shadow" is

   ____

   ____.

2. The moral of "The Dog and His Shadow" is similar to the

   lesson in ______________________________________

   because both stories ___________________________

   ____.

3. Which story do you think teaches this lesson better?

   ____

   ____

   ____

4. Why do you think many stories teach the same moral?

   ____

Introduce "The Dog and the Wolf"

Reading Questions

Choose the answer.

1. What is the most likely reason the wolf is so skinny and hungry?
   - **A.** He hasn't been able to find enough food to eat.
   - **B.** His master hasn't given him enough food to eat.
   - **C.** He would rather starve than find enough food to eat.
   - **D.** His food has been taken away by hunters who wanted it.

2. What does the dog mean when he says to the wolf, "your wild life will be the end of you"?
   - **A.** Another wild animal might kill the wolf.
   - **B.** The wolf may be hunted by humans and killed.
   - **C.** The wolf might not be able live in the wild forever.
   - **D.** The wolf might die because he has to hunt for food.

3. What does the dog have to do for food and a place to live?
   - **A.** hunt for wild animals and bring them home
   - **B.** keep wolves away from his master's house
   - **C.** work for his master and be chained at night
   - **D.** bring home wolves to work for his master

4. Why is the hair on the dog's neck worn thin?
   - **A.** The dog doesn't get enough to eat.
   - **B.** The collar the dog has to wear rubs it off.
   - **C.** The dog rubbed his neck against something.
   - **D.** The dog won't tell the wolf how it got that way.

5. Why does the wolf decide **not** to go home with the dog at the end of the story?
   - **A.** He realizes that he doesn't like the dog or his master.
   - **B.** He's not that hungry and plans to meet the dog another day.
   - **C.** He doesn't want to be chained, even to get food and shelter.
   - **D.** He thinks there might be a better master that he can live with.

Introduce "The Dog and the Wolf"

Characters and the Moral of the Story

Answer the questions.

1. What does the dog have that the wolf does **not**?

   ____

2. What does the dog have to do that the wolf does **not**?

   ____

   ____

3. What does the wolf have that the dog does **not**?

   ____

4. Why does the dog try to convince the wolf to come live with him?

   ____

   ____

5. What choice does the wolf make in the end?

   ____

6. Why does the wolf make this choice?

   ____

Review "The Dog and the Wolf"

Convincing Characters

Write a paragraph that answers these questions: Would you rather be the dog or the wolf? Why?

In your paragraph, state your main idea in a topic sentence. Then, give two reasons for your opinion.

Introduce "The Boy Who Cried 'Wolf'"

Reading Questions

Choose the answer.

1. What is the most likely reason the boy cries "Wolf" the first time?
   - **A.** He is lonely and bored and wants something to happen.
   - **B.** He wants to find out whether or not the men can hear him.
   - **C.** He is practicing what he should do when a real wolf comes.
   - **D.** He sees a wolf near the pasture and thinks it might come closer.

2. What happens each time the boy cries "Wolf"?
   - **A.** The wolf runs away.
   - **B.** The sheep run away.
   - **C.** The boy runs into town.
   - **D.** The men come running.

3. Which word best describes how the men feel when they come to the pasture each time and find that there is no wolf?
   - **A.** worried
   - **B.** bothered
   - **C.** cheerful
   - **D.** satisfied

LITERATURE & COMPREHENSION

4. Why **don't** the men come when there really is a wolf?
   - **A.** They aren't worried that the wolf will take a sheep.
   - **B.** They can't hear the boy because he's so far away.
   - **C.** They no longer believe the boy when he calls.
   - **D.** They think the boy can take care of the wolf himself.

5. Which word best describes how the boy feels at the end of the story?
   - **A.** happy
   - **B.** angry
   - **C.** sorry
   - **D.** proud

Introduce "The Boy Who Cried 'Wolf'"

Cause and Effect

Draw a line from the cause to its effect.

Cause	Effect
The boy cries "Wolf" and there isn't one.	The men don't believe the boy.
The boy cries "Wolf" when there is a wolf.	The men rush to help and are angry.
The men don't come.	The boy stops telling lies.
The boy feels terrible because no one believed him.	The wolf kills a sheep.

Making Connections

Review "The Boy Who Cried 'Wolf'"

Compare Fables

Answer the questions.

1. Which fable—"The Dog and His Shadow," "The Dog and The Wolf," or "The Boy Who Cried 'Wolf'"—has the best moral? Why?

2. Why is this moral an important lesson to learn?

3. Tell about a time when you learned this lesson in your own life.

Introduce *Buddy: The First Seeing Eye Dog*

Reading Questions

Choose the answer.

1. What is this book about?
   - **A.** German shepherds that are raised as pets for people
   - **B.** German shepherds that learn how to climb the Swiss Alps
   - **C.** German shepherds that are trained to do important work
   - **D.** German shepherds that spend their lives running and playing

2. What is the setting of Chapter 1?
   - **A.** a place called Fortunate Fields, in the Swiss Alps, a long time ago
   - **B.** a place called Fortunate Fields, in the Swiss Alps, in modern times
   - **C.** a place called Fortunate Fields, in America, a long time ago
   - **D.** a place called Fortunate Fields, in Germany, a long time ago

LITERATURE & COMPREHENSION

3. Why does Dorothy Eustis go to Germany in Chapter 2?
   A. to get more German shepherds and bring them to Fortunate Fields
   B. to see the school where dogs are trained as guides for blind soldiers
   C. to see how people live in Germany to compare their lives to those of Americans
   D. to learn more about how to care for her own German shepherds

4. What word best describes how Dorothy feels at the end of Chapter 2?
   A. unhappy
   B. frustrated
   C. bored
   D. excited

5. Why was Kiss chosen to be the first dog guide?
   A. She was a slow walker, which was good for someone who is blind.
   B. She liked to play and have fun with her trainer, Jack Humphrey.
   C. She learned quickly to obey commands, which was the most important rule.
   D. She was strong and could move objects and other dangers out of the way.

Explore *Buddy: The First Seeing Eye Dog* (A)

Reading Questions

Choose the answer.

1. Why does Buddy's harness have a handle?
   - **A.** It helps Morris feel when Buddy slows down or changes direction.
   - **B.** Morris holds on to it because Buddy doesn't wear a leash.
   - **C.** Morris uses it to pull on Buddy when she goes too fast or the wrong way.
   - **D.** It prevents Buddy from sniffing things and playing with other dogs.

2. What does Buddy do at the gate in Chapter 5?
   - **A.** She barks to be let in.
   - **B.** She stops because the gate is closed.
   - **C.** She turns away because dogs aren't allowed.
   - **D.** She walks through the gate but Morris doesn't want to go in.

3. Why doesn't Jack tell Morris about the stairs in Chapter 5?
   - **A.** He doesn't see the stairs in time to warn Morris about them.
   - **B.** He wants to test whether Buddy is using the right signals.
   - **C.** He thinks Morris should know about the stairs.
   - **D.** He wants Morris to learn to pay attention to Buddy.

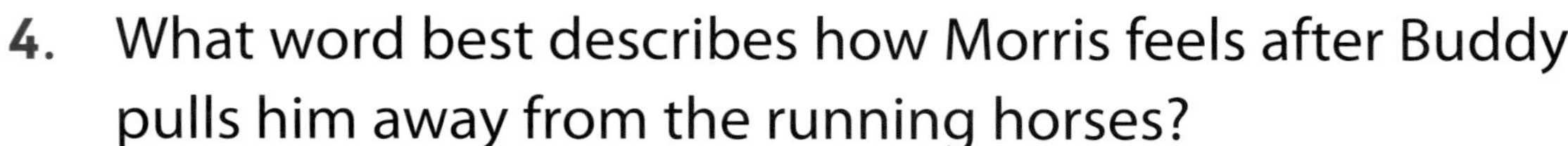

4. What word best describes how Morris feels after Buddy pulls him away from the running horses?
   - **A.** angry
   - **B.** thankful
   - **C.** confused
   - **D.** embarrassed

5. How does Morris know where he's going in the town in Chapter 6?
   - **A.** Buddy knows where he wants to go and leads him.
   - **B.** People on the street tell him the way to the barbershop.
   - **C.** He uses the sounds and smells on the streets to guide him.
   - **D.** He feels his way along the walls of the buildings.

6. Why does Morris say at the end of the Chapter 6 that he is really free?
   - **A.** No one is going to make him stay at Fortunate Fields anymore.
   - **B.** He doesn't need other people to get around because he has Buddy.
   - **C.** He will no longer have to live in a special hospital for blind people.
   - **D.** He is going home to America, where everyone is free to do what they want to.

Explore *Buddy: The First Seeing Eye Dog* (B)

Reading Questions

Choose the answer.

1. Why **doesn't** Buddy try to give Morris his wallet right away?
   - A. She doesn't know the wallet belongs to Morris.
   - B. She is obeying Morris's command to go forward.
   - C. She likes carrying something that belongs to Morris.
   - D. She knows Morris can't carry his own wallet.

2. What do the reporters think when Morris says Buddy can lead blind people?
   - A. They don't believe his story.
   - B. They think Buddy is wonderful.
   - C. They're not interested in his story.
   - D. They remember other dogs like Buddy.

3. Why is Buddy's "biggest test" crossing West Street in New York?
   - A. Morris and Buddy haven't had much practice crossing streets together.
   - B. Buddy doesn't know her way around New York and won't know where to go.
   - C. West Street is dangerous and difficult to cross, even for a person who can see.
   - D. Buddy has to cross the street with a lot of reporters watching and taking pictures.

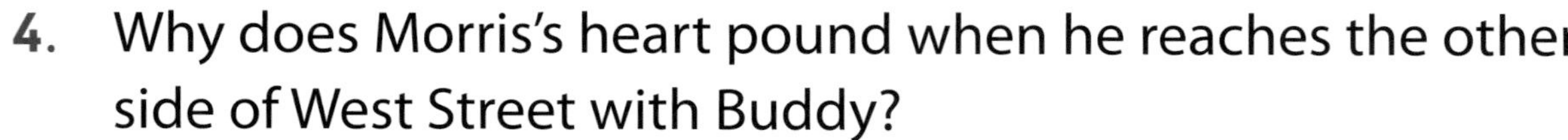

4. Why does Morris's heart pound when he reaches the other side of West Street with Buddy?

   A. He has just run across the street.

   B. He is very afraid crossing the street.

   C. He is very excited to be in New York City.

   D. He is worried that something is wrong with Buddy.

5. How does Morris feel when people stare at Buddy and him?

   A. bothered

   B. nervous

   C. curious

   D. proud

Review *Buddy: The First Seeing Eye Dog*

Reading Questions

Choose the answer.

1. How does Buddy help Morris in his work selling insurance?
   A. Morris uses Buddy in his advertising posters.
   B. People like Buddy, so they buy more from Morris.
   C. Buddy helps Morris get around to make more sales.
   D. Buddy carries all the papers Morris needs for his work.

2. What is The Seeing Eye?
   A. Morris's special nickname for Buddy
   B. the name of Dorothy Eustis's dog guide school
   C. the name of the trainer at Dorothy Eustis's school
   D. the name of the harness used by dog guides

3. In what year did The Seeing Eye open in Nashville?
   A. 1929
   B. 1931
   C. 1936
   D. 1938

4. Why does Morris like to tell newspaper reporters and other people about Buddy?
   A. He makes money when people pay him to tell his story.
   B. He wants to get more people to buy insurance from him.
   C. He is proud and wants people to know about dog guides.
   D. He wants everyone to own and train dog guides like Buddy.

5. Why does Morris name all of his guide dogs Buddy?
   A. He can't tell the difference between the dogs.
   B. He thinks Buddy is a good name for a dog guide.
   C. All of the dog guides are good friends to Morris.
   D. He loved the first Buddy and wants to honor her.

Review *Buddy: The First Seeing Eye Dog*

Sequence of Events

Write the most important event from each chapter.

Chapter 1: Gala and Kiss are

Chapter 2: Dorothy Eustis learns

Chapter 3: Kiss becomes

Chapter 4: Morris learns

Chapter 5: Morris learns

Chapter 6: Morris gets

Chapter 7: Buddy helps

Chapter 8: Morris and Buddy help

Chapter 9: Buddy gets old

Making Connections

Review *Buddy: The First Seeing Eye Dog*

Write a Book Review

Write a book review of *Buddy: The First Seeing Eye Dog*.

LITERATURE & COMPREHENSION

Introduce "Animal Helpers"

Reading Questions

Choose the answer.

1. What is the main idea of the article?
   - **A.** Monkeys can be trained to help people who cannot move very well.
   - **B.** Both miniature and large horses can be used to help people move around.
   - **C.** Sometimes dogs visit sick people in hospitals or elderly people in nursing homes.
   - **D.** Animals can help people who are sick or cannot do things for themselves.

2. Which of the following is a detail that supports the main idea?
   - **A.** Dogs can be trained to help people who are blind.
   - **B.** Most people like animals.
   - **C.** Some people are allergic to dogs.
   - **D.** Many hospitals do not allow pets.

3. How do full-size horses help people with weak muscles?
   - **A.** The horses are nice to pet and talk to.
   - **B.** The horses pull people who can't walk.
   - **C.** Riding a horse helps people get stronger.
   - **D.** The horses carry things that are too heavy.

4. What is the most likely reason that dogs help sick patients feel better?

   A. Dogs can bring patients their medicine.

   B. Dogs help patients relax and be happy.

   C. Dogs clean up germs when they lick people.

   D. Dogs help pain go away when people pet them.

5. Which is the most likely reason that monkeys are used to help people do simple jobs?

   A. Monkeys are smart and can use their hands like people do.

   B. Monkeys do not need training to do special jobs around a house.

   C. Monkeys are friendlier than dogs or cats and make better pets.

   D. Monkeys are smaller than horses and fit better inside a home.

Introduce "Animal Helpers"

Problems and Solutions

Write each problem from the article and its solution.

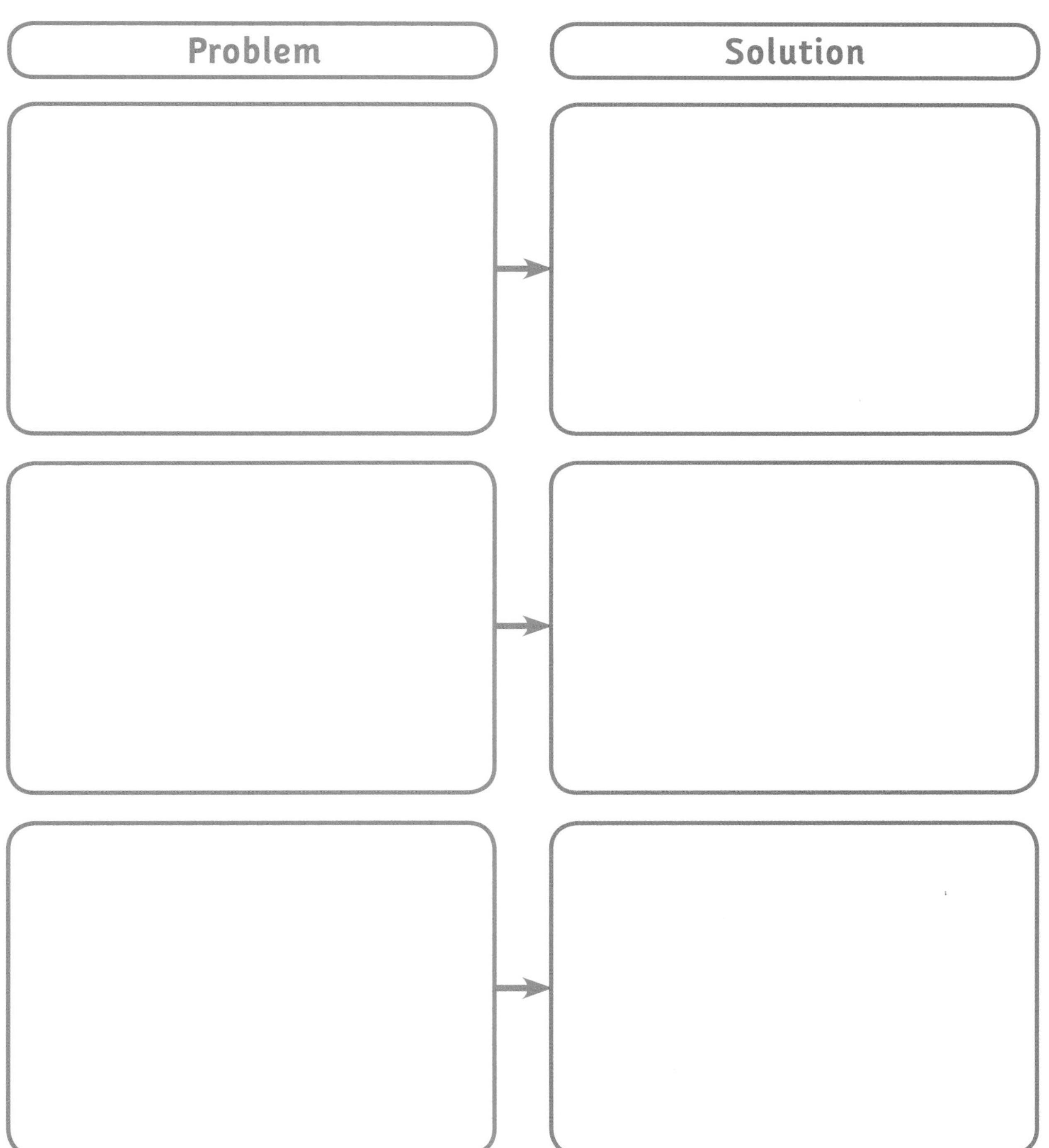

Review "Animal Helpers"

Write Captions

Examine the pictures in the article. Write a caption for the given picture.

1. picture of a sick boy and a dog, page 50

   My Caption: ____

   ____

2. picture of a blind person and a guide dog, page 52

   My Caption: ____

   ____

3. pictures of blind people with miniature horses, page 53

   My Caption: ____

   ____

4. picture of a man with a helper monkey, page 56

   My Caption: ____

   ____

5. picture of a sick boy and a dog, page 57

   My Caption: ____

Writing Skills

Learn

What Is an Adjective?

Describing Words

Guided Exercises

Describing words called **adjectives** tell size, shape, color, or other details about a noun.

The little brown and black duck waddled.

- Point to the underlined noun that tells what waddled.
- Point to the adjectives that are circled. They tell what the duck looks like.

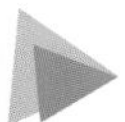

The duck waddled in the tall, green grass.

- Underline the noun that tells where the duck waddled.
- Circle two adjectives that describe the place.

Now complete the picture of the duck in the grass. Use all the clues from the sentences.

WRITING SKILLS

Try It

What Is an Adjective?

Find Adjectives

Circle the adjective or adjectives in the sentence.

1. The brown twig falls.
2. A cute young bird lands on the ground.
3. The little bird pecks at the broken twig.
4. It lets out a short, happy tweet.
5. The bird grabs the small and useful wood.

Read the word in the shape. Use brown to color each shape that has an adjective. Solve the riddle.

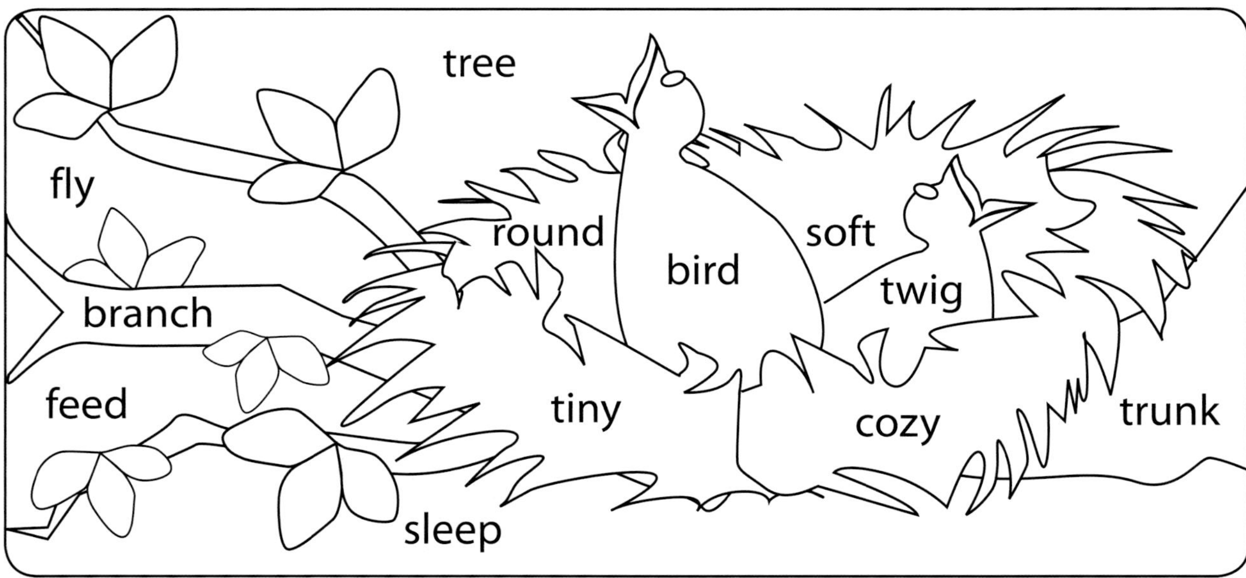

6. The bird picked up the twig for a reason. What was it?

____

WRITING SKILLS

Learn

Articles

A, An, The

Guided Exercises

A, *an*, and *the* are **articles**. Use *a* when a word begins with a consonant sound and *an* when a word begins with a vowel. Use *the* in front of a specific noun.

WRITING SKILLS

- **An ant is on a book on the table.**
  The nouns in the sentence are underlined. The words that are circled are **articles**.
- **I read a book about an artist. The pictures were colorful.**
  Underline the nouns in the sentence. Circle the words before them. These are the **articles**.

In the pair of sentences, circle the sentence that has the correct article.

1. That is the library. — That is an library.
2. It's near a oak tree. — It's near an oak tree.
3. An bus waits nearby. — A bus waits nearby
4. Open the door. — Open an door.

Try It

Articles

Use Articles

Circle each group of words where the article is used correctly.

1. an old tree
2. the monkey
3. a helicopter
4. an elf
5. the old shed
6. a umpire
7. an banana
8. the artist
9. a tunnel
10. an exit
11. the red roof
12. a ugly bug
13. an icy igloo
14. a basketball

In the pair of sentences, circle the sentence that has the correct article.

15.	A shark swims.	An shark swims.
16.	Jeff peeled an apple.	Jeff peeled a apple.
17.	Who baked an muffin?	Who baked the muffin?
18.	It's an eagle!	It's a eagle!

WRITING SKILLS

Show Me

Alexander's Descriptive Paragraph

Use Alexander's descriptive paragraph as you work through the lessons in the unit.

I love when it snows. The snowflakes melt on my tongue. The white snow sparkles. It covers everything like a blanket. I like to jump in the soft fluffy piles of snow. I roll in the snow until I look like a snowman. I wear my heavy jacket, snow pants, a knit hat, a long, fuzzy scarf, thick rubber boots, and red mittens. I hear the ice cracking under my feet. I love to feel the frozen winter air. I see and hear kids playing in the snow. When it is time to go inside, I can smell and taste sweet hot cocoa.

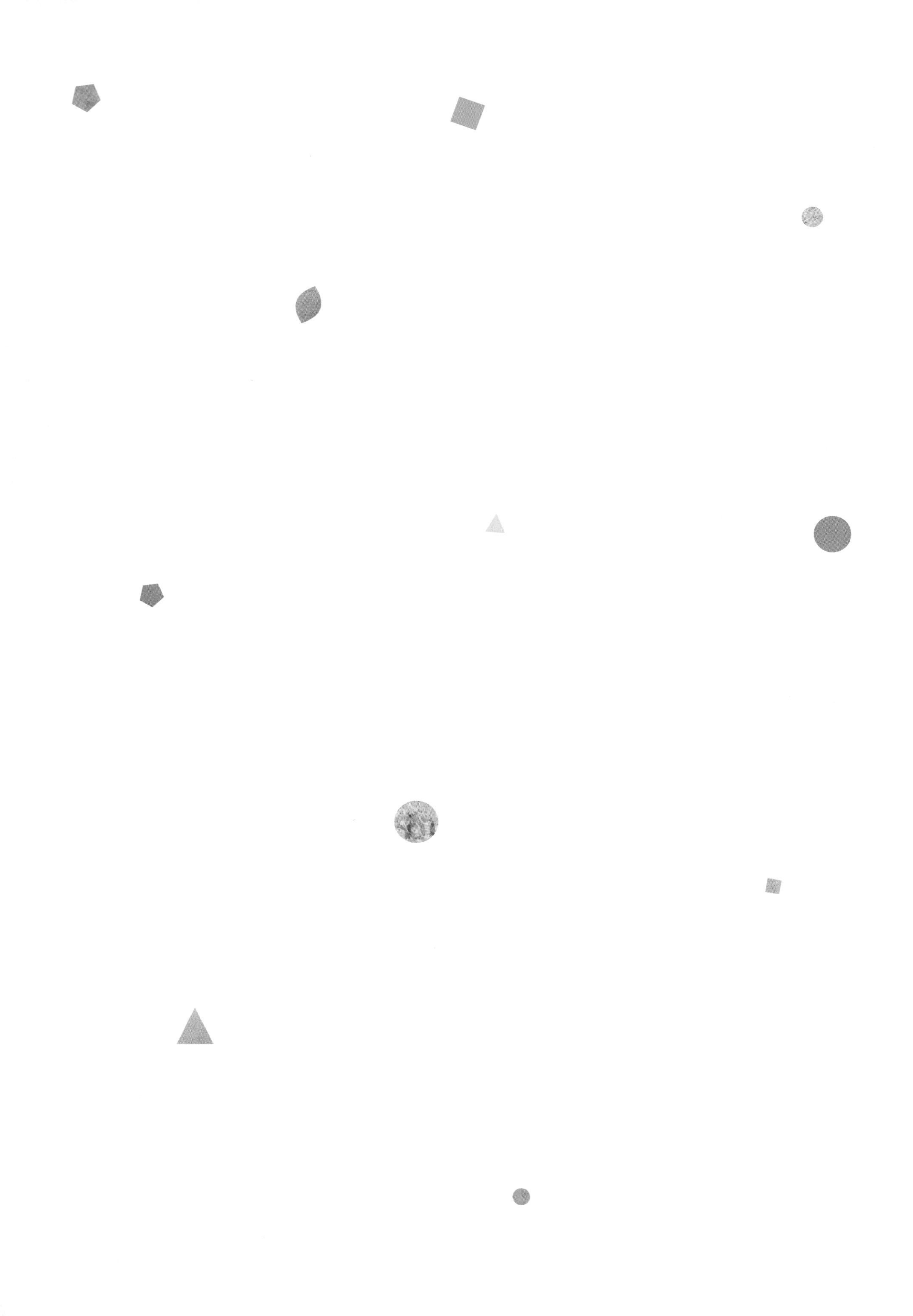

Learn

Show Me

Show, Don't Tell

Guided Exercises

Showing language creates pictures in the reader's mind. The words describe or show something instead of telling about it.

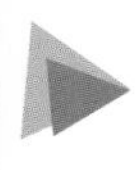

It covers everything like a blanket. I like to jump in the soft fluffy piles of snow.

- What comparison does Alexander make? Underline it.
- What adjectives does Alexander use to show what snow looks like? Circle them.

Write two sentences that describe something outside. Use words and adjectives that show what you see and use a comparison.

WRITING SKILLS

Try It

Show Me

Choose a Topic

WRITING SKILLS

Brainstorm a few topics about which you might like to write. Select one of the topics that you brainstormed and freewrite about it. Write everything you can, and do not worry about choosing the right words.

Learn

Plan a Description

Add Details to a Graphic Organizer

Guided Exercises

A **graphic organizer** can help you plan a description. It shows the main idea and descriptive words for the details.

Alexander used a graphic organizer to plan his paragraph. He wrote his main idea and planned descriptive details.

- Point to the main idea.
- Point to a supporting detail.

WRITING SKILLS

What descriptive words did Alexander add to his graphic organizer? Look at his paragraph to help you.

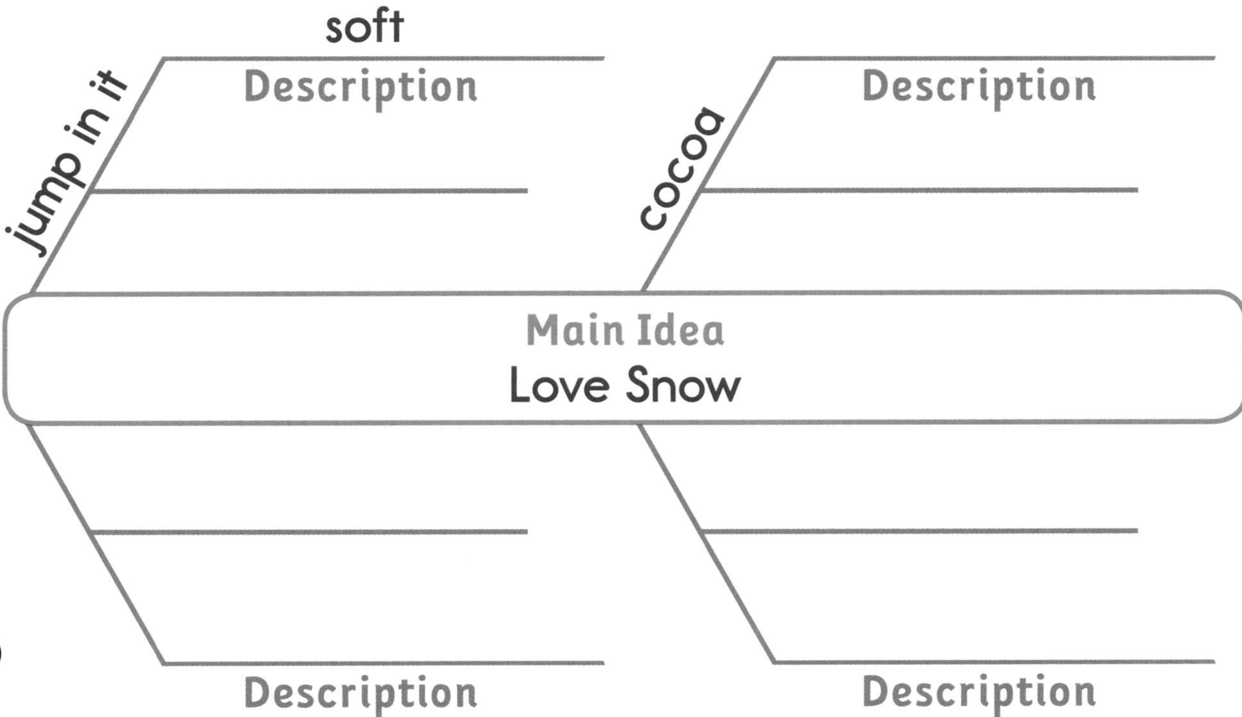

Try It

Plan a Description

Use a Graphic Organizer

Use the graphic organizer to plan your paragraph. Choose a main idea and four details from your freewriting. Then, add descriptive words, phrases, or a comparison to describe each detail.

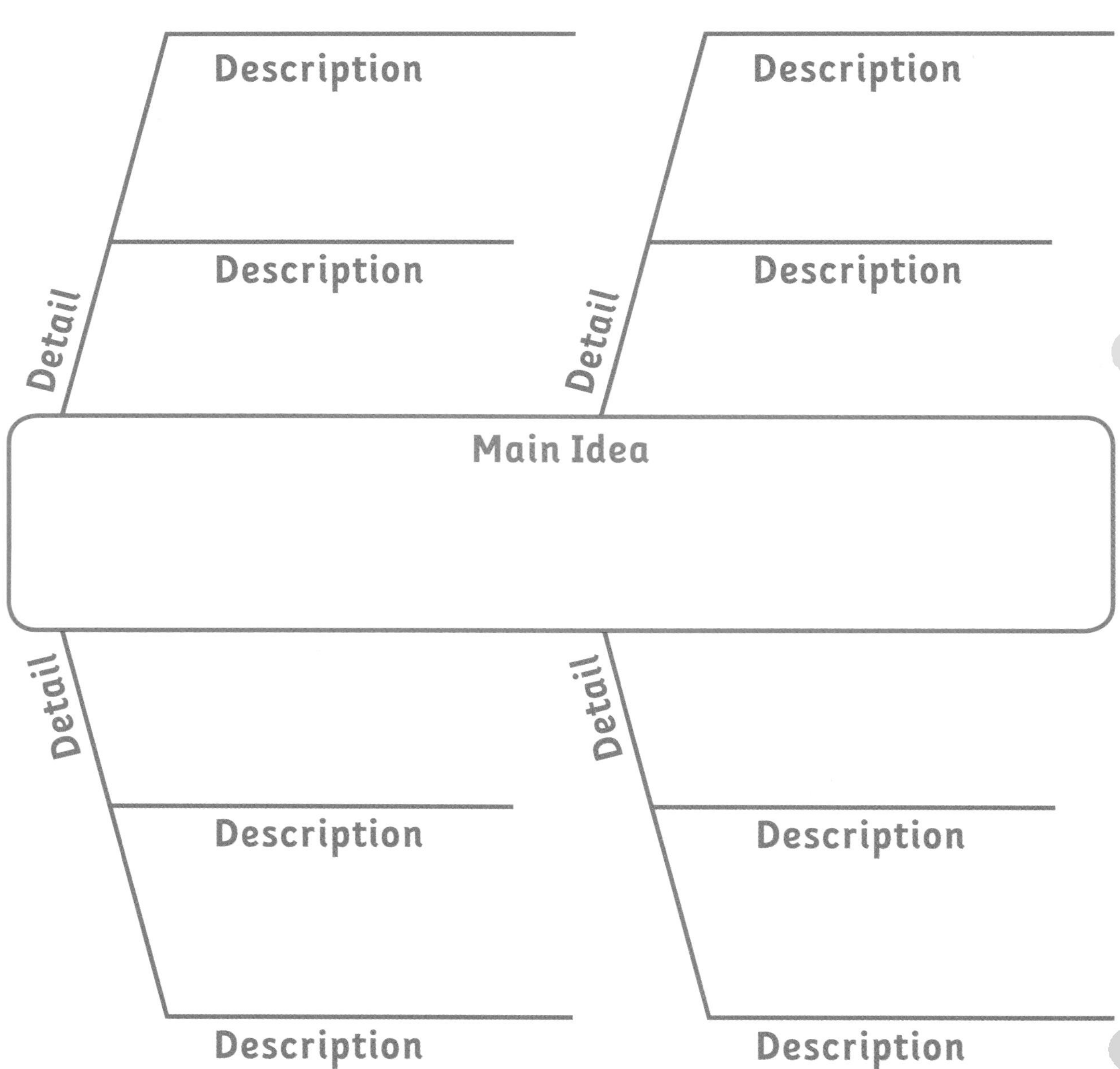

Learn

Organize Your Writing

Pattern of Organization

Guided Exercises

A **pattern of organization** is the order in which the details are arranged in a paragraph.

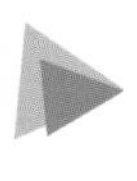

Alexander's paragraph begins with the main idea that he loves snow. Then, he tells what he does in the snow, what he wears, and what he sees and hears.

Are Alexander's details in time order, place order, or order of importance? Circle one.

WRITING SKILLS

Use place or spatial order to put the details in order. Number the sentences to match the pattern.

_____ We saw a large kitchen at the front. _____ In the back, there was a room with a piano. _____ Next to the kitchen, we saw a dining room with a table. _____ We visited a famous home.

Match the description to the best form of organization.

1.	reasons I like my new bicycle	time order
2.	the best day I ever had	order of importance
3.	my favorite reading spot	place order

Try It

Organize Your Writing

Write Your Draft

Write a draft of your paragraph. Use ideas from your graphic organizer. Choose a pattern of organization and write your sentences in that order.

WRITING SKILLS

Get Ready

Revise a Description

Revising Checklist

WRITING SKILLS

Use the checklist to revise your writing.

- ☐ Does the topic sentence state the main idea?
- ☐ Do all of the sentences tell about the main idea?
- ☐ Did I add details about the main idea?
- ☐ Did I use sensory and showing language?
- ☐ Did I include a comparison?
- ☐ Did I use an appropriate organizational pattern?
- ☐ Are there transition words to connect sentences?
- ☐ Do the sentences flow from one to the other?
- ☐ Is there a strong concluding sentence?

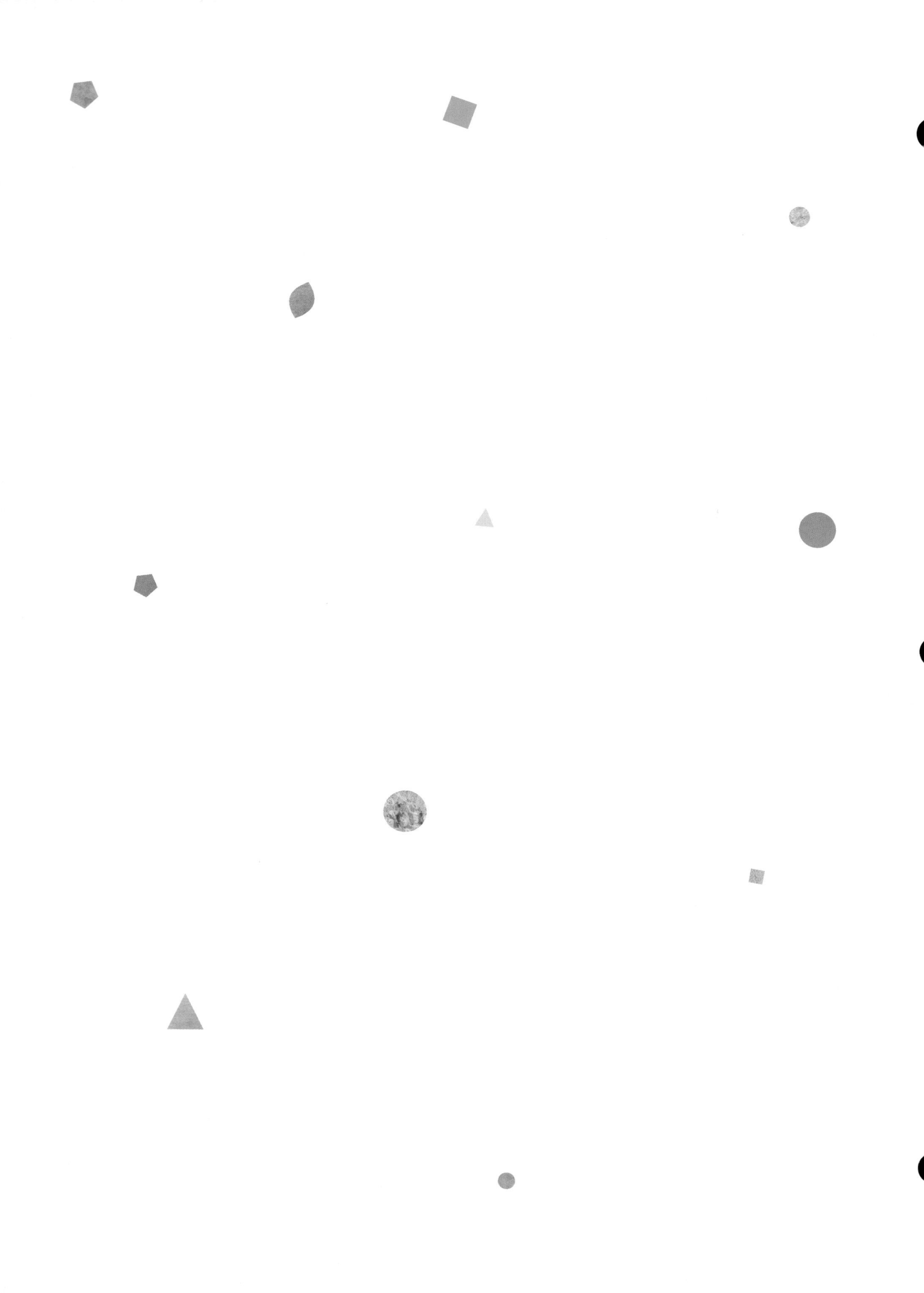

Learn

Revise a Description

Use the Five Senses

Guided Exercises

Sensory details are descriptive details that appeal to the five senses. They tell what you see, hear, touch, smell, or taste.

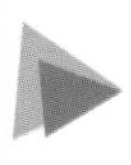

I hear the ice cracking under my feet. I love to feel the frozen winter air. I see and hear kids playing in the snow.

- Underline the sensory details in these sentences from Alexander's paragraph.
- What are two things from Alexander's paragraph that you can feel with your tongue?

WRITING SKILLS

Add sensory details to the sentences. Then, describe an orange to someone who has never seen one.

1. I smell food.

____

2. He hears the dog.

____

3. We see a tree.

____

4. ____

Try It

Revise a Description

Revise Your Description

Use the Revising Checklist to help you revise your paragraph. Mark changes on the draft. Use this space to write new sentences.

WRITING SKILLS

Write Now

Polish and Publish a Description

Publish Your Description

Write a clean, final copy of your description. Write a title for your paragraph on the first line. You may draw a picture to go with your paragraph in the space on the next page.

WRITING SKILLS

Reward

Draw a picture of what you are describing in your paragraph.

Peer Interaction

Polish and Publish a Description

Tell Me About My Description

Have another person read your descriptive paragraph and answer the questions.

1. Does the paragraph have a main idea? What is it?

____

____

2. Does the topic sentence express the main idea? Write the topic sentence here.

____

____

3. Do all of the sentences in the paragraph support the main idea? If not, which sentences are **not** focused on the main idea?

____

____

4. Are there details to support the main idea? Write some of them.

____

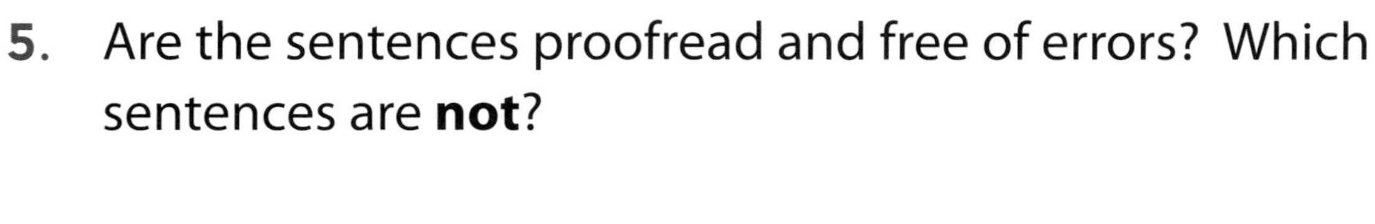

5. Are the sentences proofread and free of errors? Which sentences are **not**?

6. Are the words interesting and colorful to read? Do they paint a picture in your mind? Choose a detail or two that particularly stands out and makes a picture in your mind.

7. Did the writer use the five senses to describe the topic? Which senses are **not** included?

8. Did the writer use a comparison in the description? What is it?

9. Is the writing neat and easy to read?

10. How could the writing be improved?

Learn

What Is an Adverb?

Adverbs of Time

Guided Exercises

An **adverb** describes a verb. An adverb may tell when something happens.

Rob skated today.

The verb *skated* tells what Rob did. The adverb *today* is underlined. It tells when Rob skated.

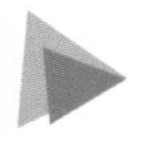

Beth performed last in her group.

Circle the verb that tells what Beth did. Underline the adverb that tells when Beth did it.

Circle the verb and underline the adverb in the sentence.

1. Call me later.
2. The ship sailed yesterday.

Each word group has a verb and an adverb. Underline each adverb that tells when.

3. pack today
4. go soon
5. leave late
6. pay now
7. work daily
8. stay tonight
9. sing softly
10. vote early
11. speak loudly

WRITING SKILLS

Try It

What Is an Adverb?

When Did It Happen?

The verb in the sentence is underlined. Circle the adverb that tells when.

1. Tina made a sandwich yesterday.
2. My dog always growls.
3. I woke early.
4. Mr. Arnold often plants beans.
5. We watched a movie today.
6. Our team plays tomorrow.
7. Lightning strikes often.
8. Our door never opens.
9. Tom will go to the store soon.
10. The game ended late.

Reward

Draw a picture to show what is happening in one of the sentences.

WRITING SKILLS

Learn

More Adverbs

Adverbs of Manner

Guided Exercises

An **adverb** describes a verb. An adverb may tell how an action happens.

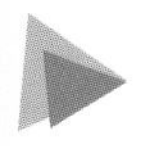

Chang ran quickly.

The verb *ran* tells what Chang did. The adverb *quickly* is underlined. It tells how Chang ran.

Jo easily won the race.

Circle the verb that tells what Jo did. Underline the adverb that tells how Jo did it.

Circle the verb and underline the adverb in the sentence.

1. Cara skipped joyfully.
2. We happily eat the pizza!

Each word group has a verb and an adverb. Underline each adverb that tells how.

3. walk softly
4. work today
5. neatly write
6. smile nicely
7. laugh easily
8. visit soon
9. clap now
10. heavily sigh
11. row strongly

WRITING SKILLS

Try It

More Adverbs

How Did It Happen?

The verb in the sentence is underlined. Circle the adverb that tells how.

1. Rosa <u>slept</u> soundly.
2. The cat <u>leaped</u> gracefully onto the bed.
3. Tom carefully <u>placed</u> the lid on the cookie jar.
4. The jar suddenly <u>fell</u>.

Choose the adverb that tells how something happened.

5. Mitzi (always, quickly) opened the gift.
6. Jacob screamed (loudly, today).
7. Darla (softly, soon) whispered in the baby's ear.
8. The puppy curled up (now, lazily) in its bed.
9. The spider moved (quietly, then) up the wall.

Write a sentence about yourself. Use the adverb *slowly* in your sentence.

10. ______________________________

____

WRITING SKILLS

Learn

Adjective or Adverb?

Which Is It?

WRITING SKILLS

Guided Exercises

An **adjective** describes a noun.
An **adverb** describes a verb.

The slow train stopped.

The noun is underlined. The adjective points to the noun. The word *slow* is an adjective. It describes the noun *train*.

The train stopped slowly.

The verb is underlined. The adverb points to the verb. The word *slowly* is an adverb. It describes the verb *stopped*.

Look at the underlined word. Decide if it is a noun or a verb. Choose the adjective or adverb that can be used to describe the underlined word.

1. The (loud, loudly) dog barks.
2. Phil (quiet, quietly) left the room.
3. Monkeys swing (happy, happily) in the trees.
4. The (large, largely) tiger roared.

Try It

Adjective or Adverb?

Use Adjectives and Adverbs

Read the clue. Choose the correct word from the box, and write it in the puzzle.

softly	soft	loud	loudly

Across

1. a kind of bed
2. how a lion roars

Down

1. how to tiptoe

Choose the adjective or adverb that can be used to describe the underlined word.

4. The cat sat (lazy, lazily) in the sun.
5. The sun (warm, warmly) shined.
6. The (hot, hotly) cat moved into the shade.

WRITING SKILLS

Get Ready

Respond to Poems That Describe

What Is Poetry?

Read the poem. Look for examples of rhythm, rhyme, and sensory language.

Spring Has Come

Author unknown

Spring has come back to us, beautiful spring!
Blue-birds and swallows are out on the wing;
Over the meadows a carpet of green
Softer and richer than velvet is seen.

Up come the blossoms so bright and so gay,
Giving sweet odors to welcome the May.
Sunshine and music are flooding the air,
Beauty and brightness are everywhere.

Learn

Respond to Poems That Describe

Respond to a Poem

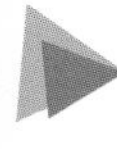

Guided Exercises

Sensory language uses words that appeal to the five senses to describe something.

Up come the blossoms so bright and so gay,
Giving sweet odors to welcome the May.

- Underline the words that help you see the blossoms.
- Circle the words that appeal to your sense of smell.

Answer the questions about the last lines of "Spring Has Come."

Sunshine and music are flooding the air,
Beauty and brightness are everywhere.

1. What does the speaker hear in May?

____

2. What does the speaker feel in May?

____

3. What other words describe springtime?

____

WRITING SKILLS

Try It

Respond to Poems That Describe

Use Sensory Language

Use your five senses to describe summer.

Summer

Summer looks like ____

____.

Summer feels like ____

____.

Summer smells like ____

____.

Summer tastes like ____

____.

Summer sounds like ____

____.

Learn

Poetic Forms and Subjects

All About Poems

Guided Exercises

Poetry has a purpose and an audience. It is made up of lines and often follows a rhythm.

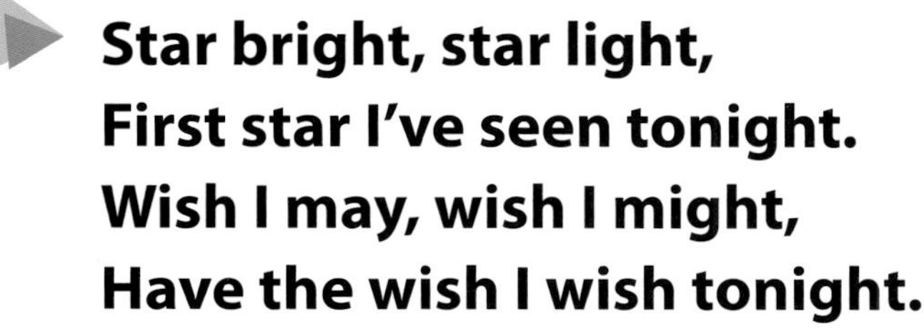

Star bright, star light,
First star I've seen tonight.
Wish I may, wish I might,
Have the wish I wish tonight.

- Who is the audience for the poem?
- What is the topic of the poem?

Answer the questions about "Star Bright, Star Light."

1. Which lines rhyme? ______________________________

2. How many syllables are in the fourth line? ______________

3. What happens in the poem? ___________________________

   ____

4. In the first line of the poem, to whom is the speaker talking?

   ____

Try It

Poetic Forms and Subjects

Plan a Descriptive Poem

Use the graphic organizer to plan your poem.

My topic ______________________________

My main idea ______________________________

My audience ______________________________

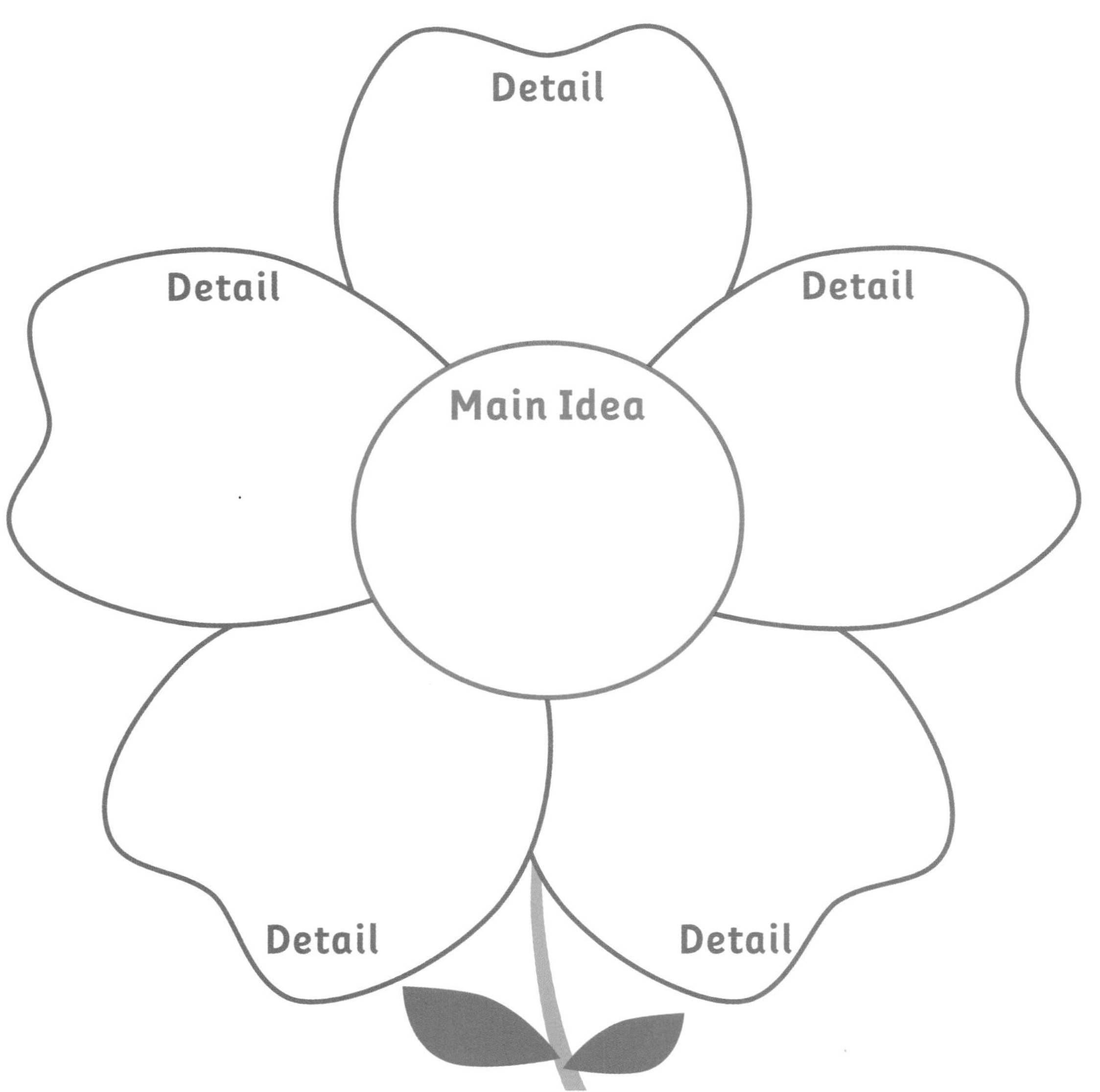

WRITING SKILLS

Get Ready

Draft a Poem

Rhyme Time

Read the poems. Choose the kind of poem you would like to write, and follow the form.

Cinquain

Dad
Strong, funny
Reading, helping, coaching
Kind, thoughtful, listens, cares
Teacher

Line 1 Subject of poem (one word)

Line 2 Two adjectives

Line 3 Three action verbs, end with *–ing*

Line 4 Four feeling words

Line 5 One word about subject (synonym or a word that sums up subject)

WRITING SKILLS

Haiku

Giant bird, wings spread,
Wheels up, tail down, nose held high,
Soars above the clouds.

Line 1 Five syllables
Line 2 Seven syllables
Line 3 Five syllables

Learn

Draft a Poem

Poetic Forms

Guided Exercises

A **cinquain** is a five-line poem that describes one subject or topic and follows a pattern. A **haiku** is a three-line poem that has an exact number of syllables in each line and describes or compares something.

The cinquain describes Dad.

- What two adjectives describe Dad?
- What kinds of words are in the third line?
- What is your favorite feeling word in the fourth line?

WRITING SKILLS

Use the haiku from Rhyme Time to answer the question.

1. What is the subject of the poem? ______________________

2. What two things are being compared in the poem?

____

3. Which word tells you that this poem is **not** really about a bird?

____

4. Which words describe both things that are being compared?

____

Try It

Draft a Poem

Write a Poem

Use your graphic organizer to write a cinquain or haiku.

WRITING SKILLS

Cinquain

____
One-word subject

____
Two adjectives

____
Three verbs ending in –ing

____
Four feeling words

____
One word about subject

Haiku

____
Five syllables

____
Seven syllables

____
Five syllables

Get Ready

Revise Your Poem

Revising Checklist for Poems

Use the checklist to revise your poem. Refer to the checklist as you work through the lessons in the unit.

- [ ] Is the poem written in the correct form?
- [ ] Does the poem have a purpose, a clear topic, and a main idea?
- [ ] Do the details describe the main idea?
- [ ] Do the lines flow from one to the other?
- [ ] Is the voice correct for the audience?
- [ ] Did I use sensory language?
- [ ] Did I use a comparison?
- [ ] Are the rhymes, rhythm, and meter correct?

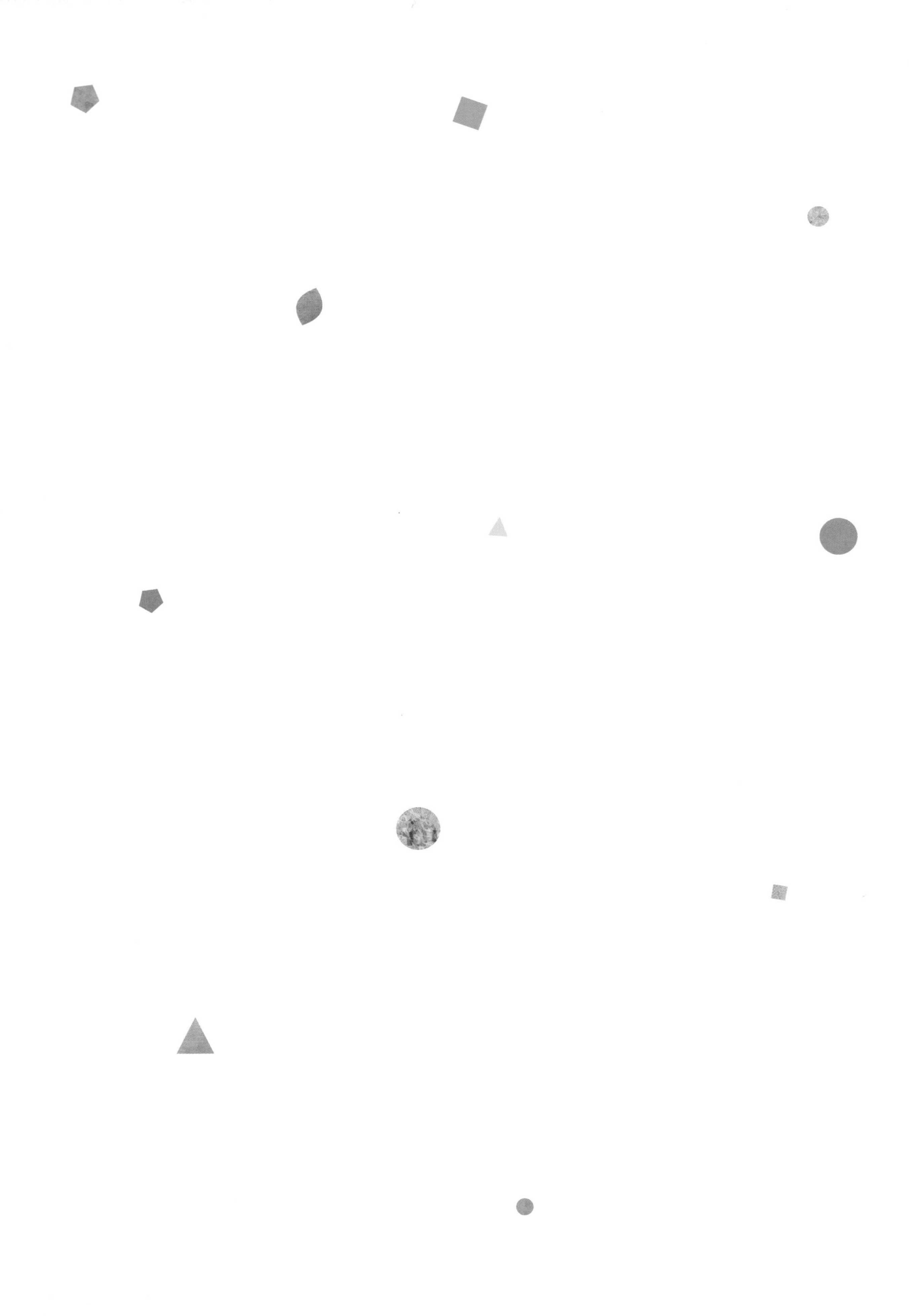

Learn

Revise Your Poem

Language and Form

Guided Exercises

Figurative language compares two unlike things for poetic effect. It is not meant to be factual.

- **The air is like a butterfly with pale blue wings.**
- **Your smile is a ray of sunshine.**

  Similes and metaphors compare two unlike things. Underline the things that are being compared in the examples.

- **The happy earth looks at the sky and sings.**

  This is personification. Underline the words that make the earth seem human.

Change the example to figurative language. Try to use personification, a simile, and a metaphor.

1. The tree branches bent.

   ____

2. The clouds were white, and the sky was blue.

   ____

3. The flowers are orange and red.

   ____

WRITING SKILLS

Try It

Revise Your Poem

Revise with a Checklist

Follow the instructions to revise your poem.

1. Reread your draft poem.
2. Where can you add sensory language to your poem? Write the new lines:

   ____

   ____

3. Where can you add a simile, a metaphor, or personification to your poem? Write the new lines:

   ____

   ____

4. Use the Revising Checklist for Poems to find more revisions. Write the changes:

   ____

   ____

5. Mark all changes on your draft poem.

Polish and Publish Your Poem

Final Poem Checklist

Use the checklist to make final changes to your poem.

- [ ] Is the language expressive?
- [ ] Did I use punctuation if my poem needs it?
- [ ] Do my words give a clear picture?
- [ ] Did I choose words that show rather than tell?
- [ ] Did I use a variety of words?
- [ ] Did I capitalize correctly?
- [ ] Are the rhythm and meter correct?
- [ ] Did I use a thesaurus to choose interesting words?
- [ ] Did I use a dictionary to check my spelling?

Write Now

Polish and Publish Your Poem

Publish Your Poem

Write a clean, final copy of your poem. Write a title for your poem. You may draw a picture to go with your poem on the next page.

Cinquain ______________________

____

____

____

____

____

Haiku ______________________

____

____

____

WRITING SKILLS

Reward.

Draw a picture to show what is happening in your poem.

WRITING SKILLS

Polish and Publish Your Poem

Tell Me About My Poem

Have another person read your poem and answer the questions.

1. What is the main idea of the poem? Which words tell you?

 ____

 ____

2. Does the title state the topic or main idea?

 ____

3. What is the poem about? Which words tell you?

 ____

 ____

4. Do the details explain the main idea? Which detail is the most descriptive?

 ____

5. Are the words interesting and colorful? Which words are your favorites?

 ____

 ____

WRITING SKILLS

6. Did the writer use words to create pictures in your mind? If so, what kind of comparison did the writer make?

____

____

7. Which senses does the poem appeal to?

____

____

8. Are the lines clear and error free? If **not**, where are the errors?

____

____

9. Is the writing neat and easy to read?

____

10. How could the writing be improved?

____

____

____

Learn

Tense of Verbs

Verbs for Different Times

Guided Exercises

Some verbs tell about actions that are happening now. Some verbs tell about actions that will happen later.

I write my name.

The verb is underlined. It tells about an action that is happening now.

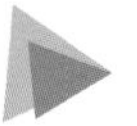

I will write my address.

Underline the two verbs. Circle the verb that tells the action will happen later.

Circle the verbs. Underline the sentence with the correct verb.

1. I go to the park next week.
2. Rain will fall tomorrow.

Fill in the blank. Use the correct form of the underlined verb.

3. Rob and Joe mix the batter now. Later, they ________________ the frosting.
4. This evening I will eat dinner. Now, I ________________ my lunch.

WRITING SKILLS

Try It

Tense of Verbs

Now and Later Verbs

Underline the verb. Write *N* if the action happens now. Write *L* if the action will happen later.

1. Monkeys hang from tree branches. ________
2. I will draw a picture of them. ________
3. Mark plays on the swings. ________
4. I watch him. ________
5. Betty climbs to the top of the slide. ________
6. Then, she will slide down. ________

Use the verb form that finishes the sentence correctly.

ride	will ride	skate	will skate

7. I ________________ at the ice rink every week.
8. We get on a bus and ________________ to the rink.
9. I ________________ tomorrow if the rink is open.
10. Later, we ________________ home with my aunt.

WRITING SKILLS

Learn

Past Tense Verbs

Verbs for the Past

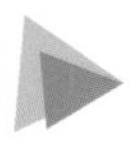

Guided Exercises

Some verbs tell about actions that already happened. These verbs usually end in *–d* or *–ed.*

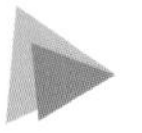

I stomped my feet.

The verb is underlined. The letters that show that the action already happened are circled.

I shouted hurray.

Underline the verb. Circle the letters that show that the action already happened.

Underline the verbs that tell about actions that already happened.

1. play
2. jumped
3. screamed
4. barked
5. lifted
6. laugh

Write the correct form of the verb to tell about an action that already happened.

7. Erin ________________ her bedroom door. (open)

8. Then, she stood and ________________. (stare)

9. The room ________________ great! (look)

WRITING SKILLS

Try It

Past Tense Verbs

What Happened at the Farm?

Underline the verb that tells about an action that already happened.

1. I visited my grandpa's farm.
2. An old cat meowed at us.

Write the correct form of the verb to tell about an action that already happened.

3. We ________________ up into the hayloft. (climb)

4. I ________________ in the hay. (jump)

5. Then, something ________________. (bang)

6. Grandpa and I ________________ toward the noise. (rush)

7. I ________________ open the gate. (pull)

8. I ________________ at the goat kicking a bucket. (laugh)

WRITING SKILLS

Get Ready

More Past Tense Verbs

Irregular Verbs List

Some verbs do not make the past tense by adding *–d* or *–ed* to the present. These past tense verbs should be learned.

Present Tense	Past Tense
hide	hid
tell	told
sit	sat
find	found
make	made
buy	bought
fall	fell
dig	dug
run	ran
eat	ate
keep	kept
write	wrote
swim	swam
drink	drank
grow	grew

Learn

More Past Tense Verbs

Irregular Past Tense Verbs

Guided Exercises

Some verbs have special forms to tell about actions that have already happened.

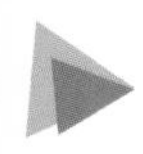

I eat popcorn today. I ate popcorn yesterday.

The verbs are underlined. The verb *ate* tells about an action that already happened. It is not formed by adding *–ed* to *eat*.

Lily swims every day. Lily swam yesterday.

Underline the verb that tells about something that already happened.

WRITING SKILLS

Underline the verb that tells about the past.

1. Ken ran into the house for a snack.
2. Nan and I drank some milk.
3. Then Nan told me a story.

Change the underlined verb so it tells about the past. Write it in the sentence.

4. Jen grows tomatoes in her garden.

   Jen ____________________ tomatoes in her garden.

5. Tim writes cookbooks.

   Tim ____________________ cookbooks.

Try It

More Past Tense Verbs

Say It, Match It, Use It

Match the verb pairs.

1.

Present	Past
write	made
hide	wrote
keep	hid
fall	kept
make	fell

Write the correct form of the verb to tell about the past.

2. Ernie ________________ the cheese. (find)
3. The worms ________________ a hole last week. (dig)
4. We ________________ a story to Jim. (tell)
5. Fran ________________ a new game. (buy)
6. The cat ________________ in the window. (sit)

WRITING SKILLS

What Is an Experience Story?

Sara's Experience Story

Use Sara's Experience Story as you work through the lessons in the unit.

Seeing Purple

I knew something was wrong. It was family night and Dad rented a movie. We all sat in the living room. I said the picture wasn't clear. Everyone else said that it was clear. Then, when Dad read me a good night story, I had trouble seeing the words. I was scared.

"I think there's something wrong," I said. "Everything looks fuzzy."

"Sara, sounds like we need to take you to the eye doctor," Dad said with a smile.

"I'm not wearing glasses," I said. "My friends will laugh at me."

The next day, I was at the eye doctor's office reading letters on a chart. The doctor was nice, but he said I needed glasses. I felt like crying. A friendly girl took me into a huge room filled with glasses of all sizes and colors. She asked, "What's your favorite color?" I said purple. She looked around and found purple glasses. I was surprised to see how pretty they were. They were light purple with swirls of dark purple. They looked just like this purple dress I used to have. I put them on and looked in the mirror. I almost smiled. They weren't bad at all. The girl hugged me and said they looked really cool on me.

A week later, I had my new glasses. I was really scared to face my friends. Mom invited them over for a play date and made lemon cookies. The cookies smelled great and melted in my mouth. We were all busy munching and crunching when Jen looked up and said, "Sara, where did you get those glasses? They are so cool!" My friends all stared at me. Then, they said they wanted glasses just like them. I guess wearing glasses is not so bad. The important thing is, when I wear my purple glasses, I can see!

Learn

What Is an Experience Story?

Guided Exercises

A **narrative** is a kind of writing that tells a story. The story can be made up or it can tell about a real experience.

A narrative has a beginning, middle, and end, and it uses transitions to connect ideas.

- What happens in the beginning of Sara's Experience Story?
- What happens in the middle of the story?
- What happens at the end?

WRITING SKILLS

Use Sara's Experience Story, "Seeing Purple," to answer the questions.

1. What is the narrative about?

____

2. Why is this important?

____

3. What is the conclusion of the story?

____

4. What important lesson does Sara learn?

____

Try It

What Is an Experience Story?

Look at an Experience Story

Use Sara's Experience Story to answer the questions.

1. What examples of descriptive language are in the story?

____

____

____

2. What sensory language is used in the story?

____

____

____

3. What transitions are used in the story?

____

4. Look at the examples of dialogue. Which characters speak in the story?

____

____

WRITING SKILLS

Learn

Brainstorm an Experience Story

Choose a Good Topic

Guided Exercises

The **plot** is what happens in a story. It is a sequence of events that happen in a certain order.

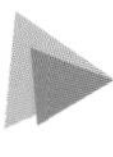

"Seeing Purple" tells about going to the eye doctor and getting glasses.

- How would the plot change if Sara's eyesight were fine?
- What would happen if the events were written in a different order?

Choose the best plot for the story.

1. The Johnson family had a barbecue.

   A. The family had fun.

   B. A raccoon took their food.

2. Mrs. White is 90 years old and lives alone.

   A. The neighbors surprise her and paint her house.

   B. The neighbors say hello when they walk by.

3. Jason didn't know how to swim and was afraid of the water.

   A. He never went to the beach.

   B. He took swimming lessons and faced his fears.

Try It

Brainstorm an Experience Story

Brainstorm!

Brainstorm story ideas. Write two experiences with two details and a conclusion or message for each. Choose the best idea for a story.

Experience ______________________________

Details

1. ______________________________

2. ______________________________

Conclusion ______________________________

Experience ______________________________

Details

1. ______________________________

2. ______________________________

Conclusion ______________________________

Best story idea ______________________________

____

WRITING SKILLS

Get Ready

Plan an Experience Story

Sara's Story Map

Sara completed a story map to set up the main parts of her story. Use the map as you work through the lessons in the unit.

Topic
Need glasses

Setting
home, eye doctor's office

Characters
Sara, Jake, Dad, Mom, doctor, girl, Jen, friends

Beginning
Things look fuzzy; Feel scared; Dad says go to eye doctor

Middle
Go to doctor; Get glasses; Stop for ice cream

End
Friends come; Mom bakes; Girls like glasses; Help clean up

Conclusion
No need to be afraid; Now can see better.

WRITING SKILLS

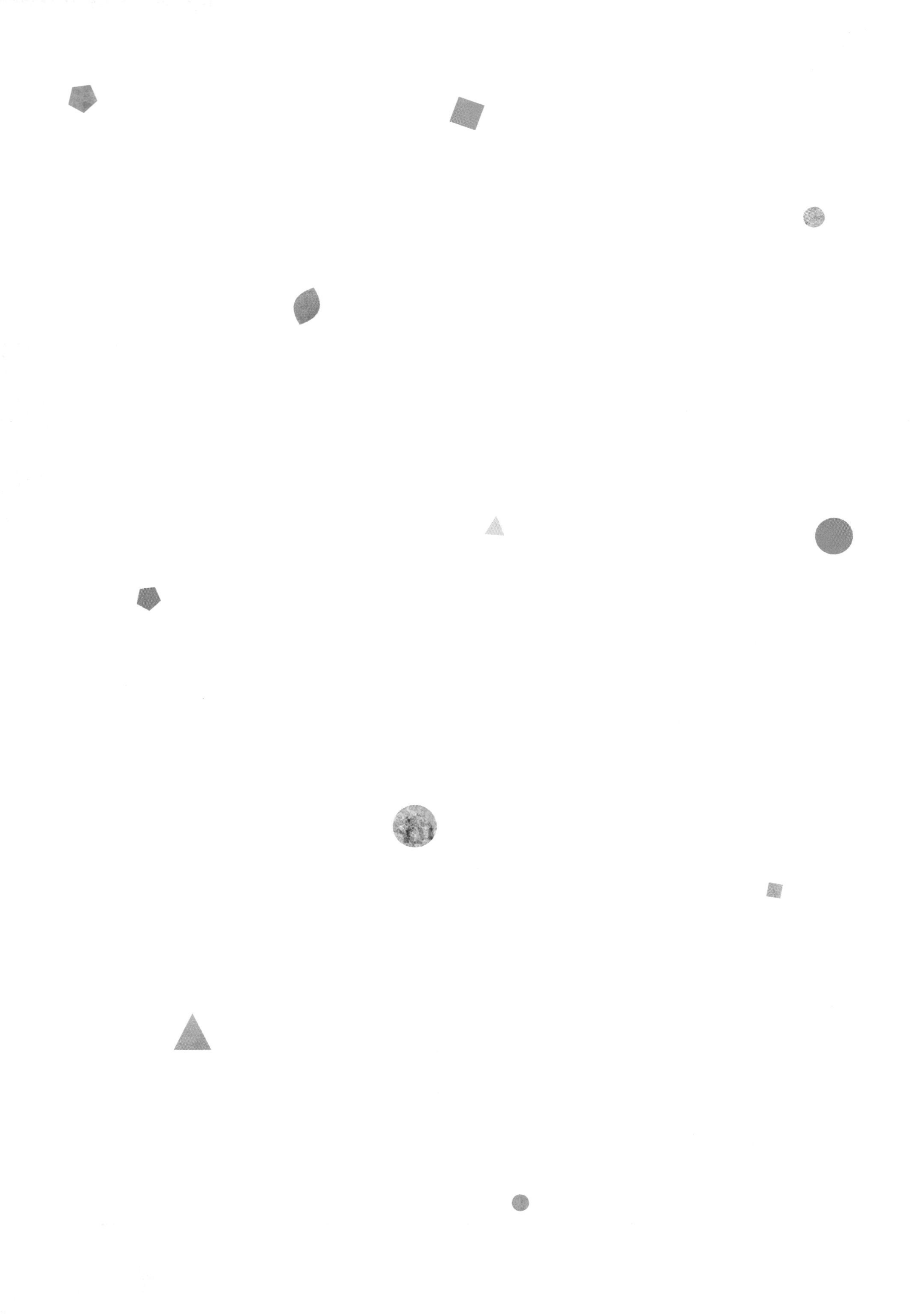

Learn

Plan an Experience Story

Use a Story Map

Guided Exercises

A **story map** is a graphic organizer that helps a writer plan a story. It shows information about the story, including the setting, the characters, and the main events.

Sara completed a story map to plan "Seeing Purple." How does the story map show the plot of the story?

WRITING SKILLS

Use Sara's Story Map and Sara's Experience Story to answer the questions.

1. Look at the setting and characters on Sara's Story Map. What is different from the final story?

____

2. Look at the first event on the map. Where does this information appear in the story?

____

3. Which detail from the middle of "Seeing Purple" is **not** on Sara's Story Map?

____

4. Which detail in the end event on the map is **not** in "Seeing Purple"?

____

Try It

Plan an Experience Story

Complete Your Story Map

Fill in the story map. Add ideas, events, and details that will help you write your story.

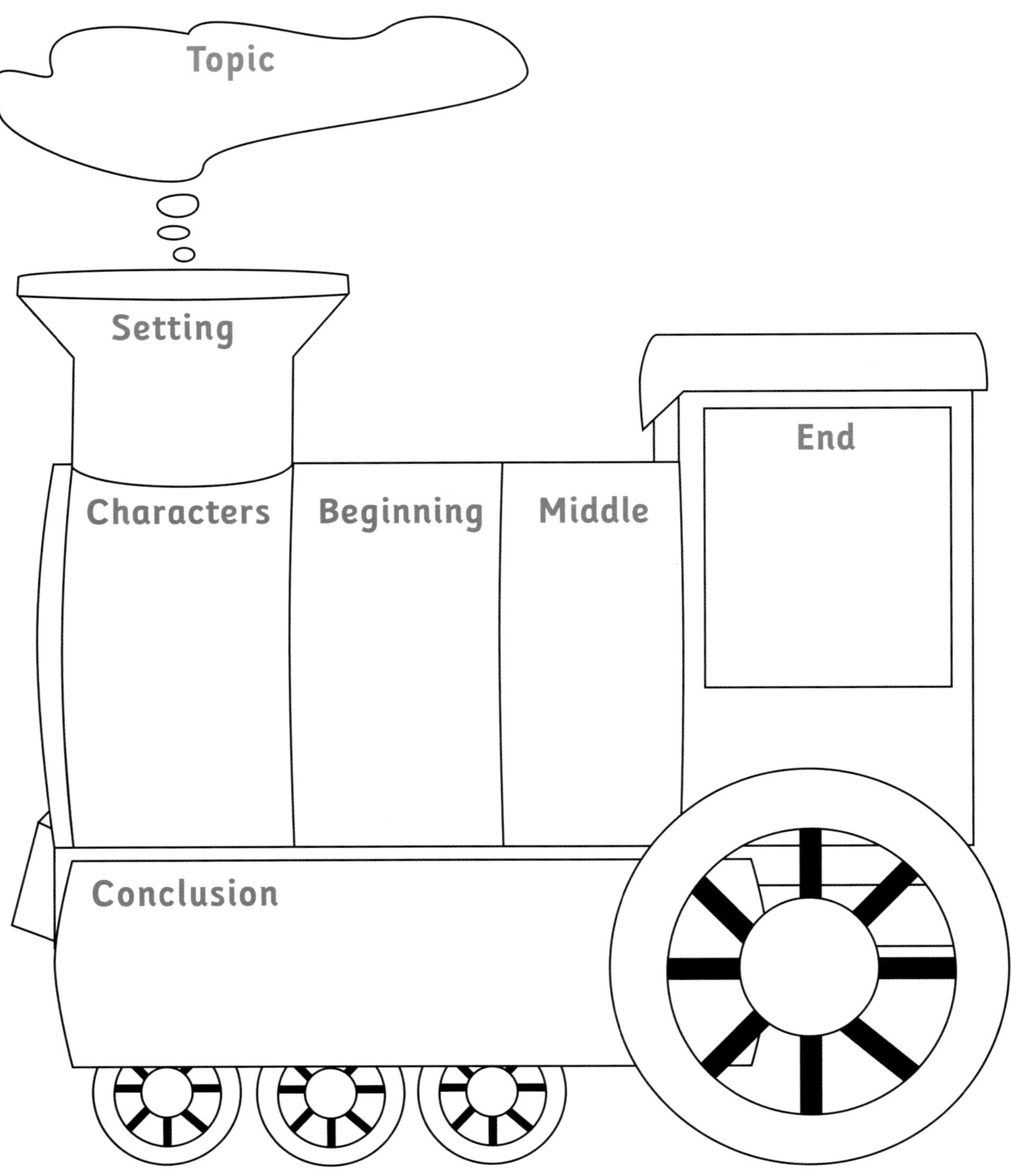

WRITING SKILLS

Learn

Draft Dialogue

Write Dialogue

Guided Exercises

Dialogue is the conversation or words spoken between two or more characters in a story. The **speaker tag** tells you who is speaking.

▶ **"I'm not wearing glasses," I said. "My friends will laugh at me."**

- "I said" is a speaker tag. It tells you that Sara is speaking. How do you know that this is dialogue?
- What does this dialogue tell you about Sara?

▶ **Tell why this part of the dialogue is important to the story: "Sara, where did you get those glasses? They are so cool!"**

Rewrite the sentence as dialogue.

1. Marco said he doesn't want to go.

____

2. Mom said dinner was ready.

____

3. Chen didn't like the color.

____

WRITING SKILLS

Try It

Draft Dialogue

Start Your Draft

Use your story map to help you write your story. Include dialogue to help tell your story. Use additional sheets of paper if you need more space to write.

WRITING SKILLS

Write Now

Complete an Experience Story

Complete Your Draft

Finish writing your draft story. You will receive feedback to help you revise it.

WRITING SKILLS

WRITING SKILLS

Learn

What Are Quotations?

Look Who's Talking

Guided Exercises

A **quotation** is the words of a character. A quotation begins and ends with **quotation marks**. **Dialogue** has quotations.

- **Carly pointed. "Grace has my bag ."**
- **Mom saw Grace with the bag. "Get your bag back before you leave."**
- **Carly nodded. "I'll ask her for it now."**

Circle the quotation marks. They show the words of a character. Underline the quotations in the dialogue.

Read the dialogue. Underline the quotations. Circle the quotation marks.

1. Jane was thirsty, so she walked into the shop. She looked around.

   The clerk smiled at her. "May I help you?"

   Jane asked, "Do you have milk?"

These sentences are quotations. Put quotation marks around them.

2. Did you hear about Sue?
3. She got a brand new telescope.
4. I can't believe it!

WRITING SKILLS

Try It

What Are Quotations?

Did You Say Something?

Write *Q* if the sentence is written as a quotation. Write *N* if the sentence is not written as a quotation.

1. The sun rises in the east. ________
2. "I wake up as soon as it is light." ________
3. "There are a lot of windows in the room." ________
4. The smell of pancakes floats upstairs. ________
5. "The pancakes will taste good!" ________

This story is about Ken and Kelly. Write quotation marks at the start and the end of each quotation.

6. Ken and Kelly are friends.
They stood by the swings. Kelly smiled.
Let's play on the swings.
Ken smiled back.
I can swing higher than you!
Then, Ken and Kelly jumped on the swings.

WRITING SKILLS

Learn

More Quotations

Tag, You're It!

Guided Exercises

Speaker tags tell who is talking. A comma comes between the speaker tag and the quotation.

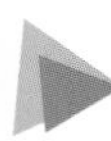

Marsha said, "Ty ate with Leo."

- The speaker tag and comma are underlined.
- The name of the person talking is circled.

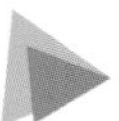

Sara asked, "What did they eat?"

- Underline the speaker tag.
- Circle the name of the person talking.

Underline the speaker tag. Circle the name of the person talking.

1. Gavin said, "I have to go to the library."
2. Molly asked, "Why are you going?"

Add a comma and quotation marks to the sentence.

3. Wilma whispered The baby is sleeping.
4. Kevin answered I will try to be quiet.
5. David whined Are we there yet?
6. Elsa scolded Be patient.

Try It

More Quotations

Put It All Together

Match the speaker tag to the quotation. Underline the name of the speaker.

1.	The officer yelled,	"Can I have a kiss?"
2.	The chef said,	"You're under arrest!"
3.	Grandma asked,	"Waaaah!"
4.	The baby cried,	"I cooked a steak."

Add a comma and quotation marks to the sentence.

5. Lou roared Don't run near the pool!
6. The doctor asked How do you feel?
7. My cousin says It's going to rain today.
8. The little boy mumbled I'm sorry I lied.
9. Coach shouted Play defense!

Reward

Get Ready

Revise for Focus

Sara's Draft Experience Story

Sara completed a draft, which she revised and proofread, before she published her story. Use Sara's draft as you work through the lessons in the unit.

WRITING SKILLS

Seeing Purple

1 I knew something was wrong. It was family night and Dad rented a movee. We all sat in the living room. I said the picture was'nt clear. Everyone else said that it was clear. Jake started to make fun of me. Then, when Dad read me a good night story, I had trouble reading the words. I was scared.

2 I"I think theres something wrong," I said. "Everything looks fuzy."

3 I"Sara, sounds like we need to take you to the eye doctor," dad said with a smile.

4 I"I'm not wearing glasses," I said. "My friends will laugh at me."

5 The next day, I was at the eye doctor. Reading letters on a chart. The doctor was nice. But he said I needed glasses. I felt like crying. A friendly girl asked, "What's your favorite color?" I said purple. She looked

around. She found purple glasses. I put them on. I looked in the mirror. I almost smiled. They weren't bad at all. The girl hugged me. The girl said they looked really cool on me. On the way home, Dad took me out for an ice cream sunday.

6 A week later, I had my new glasses. Now that I had my new glasses, I was really scared to face my friends. Mom invited them over for a play date. Mom made lemon cookies. Us were all busy eating when Jen looked up and said, "Sara, where did you get those glasses? They are so cool?" My friend all steered at me. Then they said they wanted glasses just like them. I helped Mom clean up. We sure made a mess. I guess wearing glasses is not so bad. The important thing is when I wear my purple glasses I can see!

Learn

Revise for Focus

Put Things in Focus

Guided Exercises

Writing has a **focus** when it is on track and sticks to the main idea of the story.

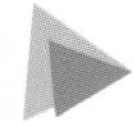

Jake started to make fun of me.

- This sentence moves away from the focus of the story.
- Why did Sara delete the sentence when she revised her draft?

WRITING SKILLS

Use Sara's Draft Experience Story to answer the questions.

1. Which sentence can be added to the end of Paragraph 1 without changing its focus? Circle it.

   A. No more family nights for me.

   B. This had happened before.

2. Which sentence can be added to Paragraph 5 without changing its focus? Circle it.

   A. I was surprised how hard it was to see the letters.

   B. I thought about the work I had to do at home.

3. Which two sentences in Paragraph 6 change its focus and should be deleted?

   ____

Try It

Revise for Focus

Focus!

Reread your draft. Use the questions to revise your draft so that it stays focused.

1. Are there any details in your story that do **not** say something about the main idea?
   A. Yes
   B. No

2. If you answered Yes, cross out those details.

3. Are there any ideas that are **not** related?
   A. Yes
   B. No

4. If you answered Yes, cross out those details.

5. Can you add any details to help focus your story?
   A. Yes
   B. No

6. Write any new sentences on your draft.

Learn

Revise for Content

What Can I Add or Delete?

Guided Exercises

Content includes the ideas and details in a piece of writing. Details can be added or deleted to make writing stronger.

They were light purple with swirls of dark purple. They looked just like this purple dress I used to have.

Why did Sara add these sentences to her story?

I helped Mom clean up. We sure made a mess.

Why did Sara delete these sentences?

Cross out four sentences that can be deleted from the story.

We all wanted a dog. We didn't want a cat. Our parents took us to an animal shelter. It was pretty far away. I wanted a small dog and my brother wanted a large one. Mom wanted a white dog and Dad wanted a black one. My friend has a tan dog. We spotted the perfect dog right away. He was medium size and black with white spots. Guess what we named him? We named him Domino. He seemed happy to see us. I wonder if he barks a lot? We were very happy to find him.

Try It

Revise for Content

Ideas and Details

Use the questions to help you add ideas, description, and dialogue.

1. Can you add details to make the story stronger?

   A. Yes **B.** No

2. If you answered Yes, add the details to your draft using coloring pencils.

3. Can you add descriptive language to be clearer?

   A. Yes **B.** No

4. If you answered Yes, add the descriptive language to your draft using coloring pencils.

5. Can you add dialogue to make the story come alive?

   A. Yes **B.** No

6. If you answered Yes, add the dialogue to your draft using coloring pencils.

7. Can you take out details that are **not** needed?

   A. Yes **B.** No

8. If you answered Yes, cross out those details.

9. Write any new sentences on your draft.

Learn

Revise for Variety in Sentences

Check Voice and Sentence Variety

Guided Exercises

Voice is the way a piece of writing sounds. Writing should sound smooth and natural. Sentences should have variety.

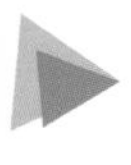

Mom invited them over for a play date. Mom made lemon cookies.

Why did Sara combine these sentences?

Revise Sara's Draft Experience Story for smoothness and variety.

1. Combine the first two sentences in Paragraph 5.

____

2. Combine the third and fourth sentences in Paragraph 5.

____

3. Combine these sentences into one: "I'm not wearing glasses. No way! No glasses!"

____

4. Rewrite these sentences so they are not so short and choppy: "I have glasses. I need glasses."

____

WRITING SKILLS

Try It

Revise for Variety in Sentences

Sentence Variety and Voice

Use the questions to revise your draft.

1. Do the sentences sound natural, like you wrote them?

   A. Yes **B.** No

2. Did you use different words in each sentence?

   A. Yes **B.** No

3. Do the sentences show variety?

   A. Yes **B.** No

4. Do you have some short sentences, some medium sentences, and some long sentences?

   A. Yes **B.** No

5. If you answered No to any of the questions, use coloring pencils to rewrite sentences on your draft.

6. Can you combine sentences?

   A. Yes **B.** No

7. If you answered Yes, use coloring pencils to combine sentences on your draft.

8. Write any new sentences on your draft.

Learn

Proofread and Polish Your Experience Story

Proofread Sara's Draft

Guided Exercises

Proofreading means fixing errors in grammar, punctuation, capitalization, and spelling.

Sara proofread Paragraph 6 of her experience story and found four errors.

- ~~Us~~ We were all busy eating when Jen looked up and said, "Sara, where did you get those glasses? They are so cool~~?~~!" My friends all ~~steered~~ stared at me.
- Sara wants to replace the word "eating" with a more descriptive word. Where should Sarah look to find a different word that means "eating"?

Find the error in the sentence and correct it.

1. It was family night and Dad rented a movee. ____________

2. I said the picture was'nt clear. ____________

3. I think theres something wrong. ____________

4. Everything looks fuzy. ____________

WRITING SKILLS

Try It

Proofread and Polish Your Experience Story

Final Checklist

Use the checklist to revise your story. Check off what you have already done. Keep revising and proofreading until you can check off all items.

WRITING SKILLS

- ☐ Did I add a title to my story?
- ☐ Are my sentences complete?
- ☐ Did I use nouns, pronouns, verbs, and adjectives correctly?
- ☐ Do my verbs agree with their subjects?
- ☐ Do my sentences have the correct end marks?
- ☐ Did I capitalize proper nouns and the first word in each sentence?
- ☐ Are apostrophes used correctly in contractions and possessives?
- ☐ Did I use sensory and showing language?
- ☐ Did I use a thesaurus to choose interesting words?
- ☐ Did I use a dictionary to check my spelling?
- ☐ Did I include dialogue and use the correct punctuation?

Publish Your Experience Story

Publish and Illustrate

Complete the clean, final copy of your story. On a separate page, draw a picture to illustrate your story.

Peer Interaction

Publish Your Experience Story

Tell Me About My Story

Have another person read your story and answer the questions.

1. What is the main idea of the story?

____

2. What happens in the beginning, middle, and end of the story?

____

____

____

3. How is the story organized? Is it in logical order or time order?

____

4. What is the setting of the story?

____

5. Who are the characters?

____

WRITING SKILLS

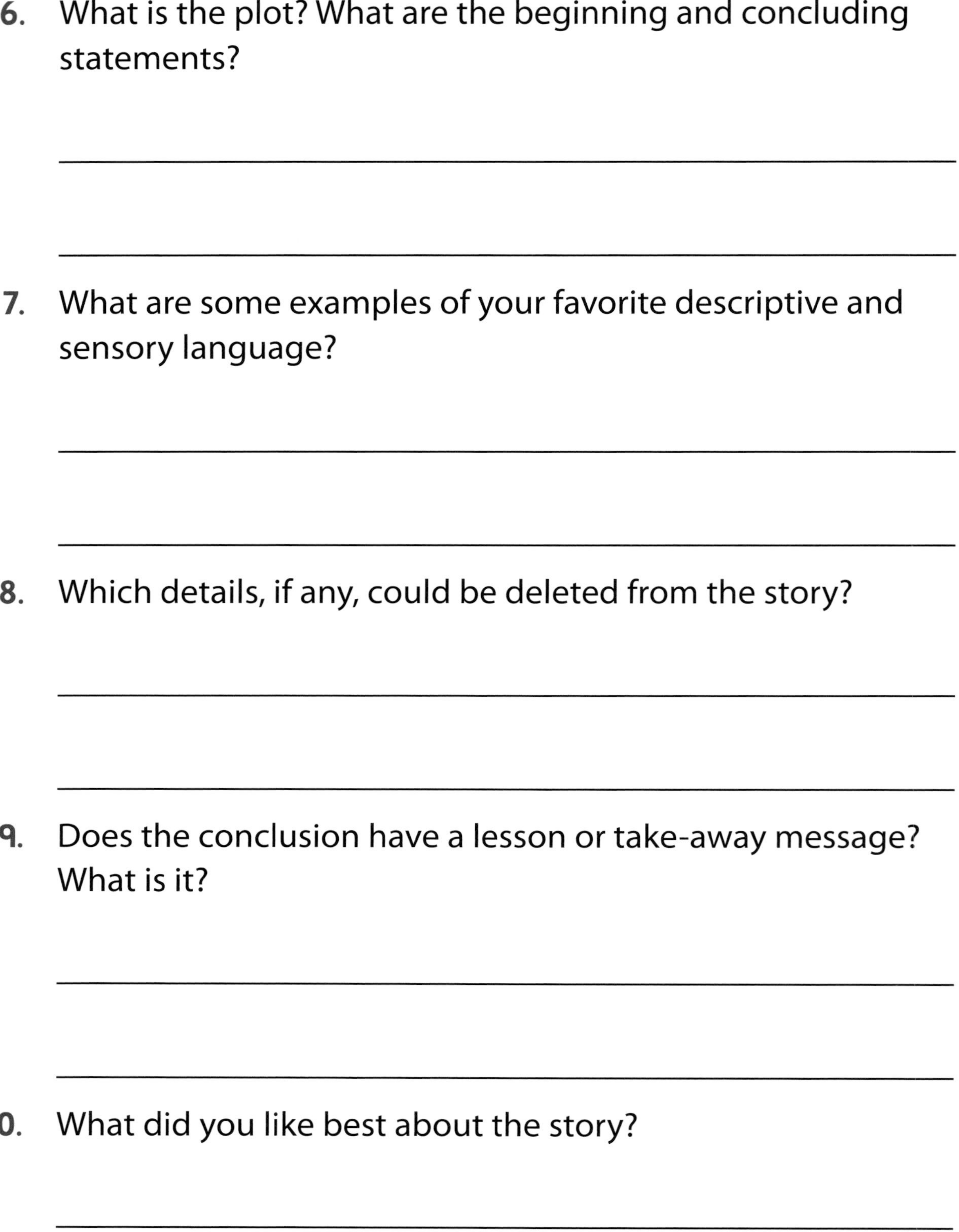

WRITING SKILLS

6. What is the plot? What are the beginning and concluding statements?

____

____

7. What are some examples of your favorite descriptive and sensory language?

____

____

8. Which details, if any, could be deleted from the story?

____

____

9. Does the conclusion have a lesson or take-away message? What is it?

____

____

10. What did you like best about the story?

____

Learn

What Is a Possessive Noun?

Who Has What?

Guided Exercises

A **possessive noun** names a person, place, or thing that has or owns something. Singular possessive nouns end in *'s*.

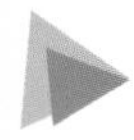

The wings of the owl are brown.

The underlined animal has or owns something. Circle what the animal has.

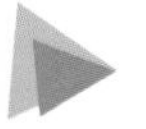

The owl's wings are brown.

Add *'s* to *owl* to make a possessive noun. It shows that the wings belong to the owl.

WRITING SKILLS

Underline the possessive noun in the sentence.

1. Everyone had fun at Victor's party.
2. Then, I tripped on the dog's leash.

Rewrite the underlined part of the sentence. Use a possessive noun.

3. The shoes that Kim has cost twenty dollars.

   ____

4. The wheels on that car are worth a lot of money.

   ____

Try It

What Is a Possessive Noun?

Spot 'Em and Shorten 'Em

Underline the possessive noun in the sentence.

1. Michael's new puppy is a mutt.
2. The puppy's name is Scraps.
3. Scraps stepped on the cat's tail today.

Rewrite the underlined part. Use a possessive noun.

4. <u>The book Vince owned</u> was thick.

   ____

5. <u>The beaches of Florida</u> are lovely.

   ____

6. You don't understand the <u>size of the piano.</u>

   ____

7. <u>The jacket that belongs to Tammy</u> is in the closet.

   ____

Make your name a possessive noun. Use it in a sentence.

8. ____________________

   ____

WRITING SKILLS

Learn

Plural Possessive Nouns

Guided Exercises

If a plural noun ends in *s*, add an apostrophe to make it possessive.

The fins of sharks are big.

The sharks have or own something. Circle what they have.

The sharks' fins are big.

Add ' after *sharks* to make a possessive noun. It shows that the fins belong to the sharks.

Underline the possessive noun in the sentence.

1. My sisters' names are Lisa, Laura, and Louise.
2. Their friends' band needs a new drummer.

Rewrite the underlined part of the sentence. Use a possessive noun.

3. The helmets that the riders own keep them safe.

____

4. The names of her brothers are Rick and Mick.

____

WRITING SKILLS

Try It

Plural Possessive Nouns

Practice, Practice, Practice

Underline the possessive noun in the sentence.

1. The actors' costumes were strange.
2. The soldiers' boots were orange.
3. All of your songs' titles are short.

Rewrite the underlined part of the sentence. Use a possessive noun.

4. The edges of the bricks are broken.

____

5. We sat next to the children of the players.

____

6. The cars my parents own are both red.

____

7. I spent the summer at the house of my cousins.

____

8. The garden of my uncles has colorful flowers.

____

WRITING SKILLS

Learn

More Plural Possessive Nouns

Make S-less Plurals Possessive

Guided Exercises

If a plural noun does not end in *s*, add *'s* to make it possessive.

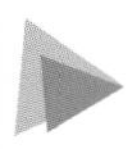

The tails the mice have are long.

The mice have or own something. Circle what the mice have.

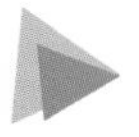

The mice's tails are long.

Add *'s* to *mice* to make a possessive noun. It shows that the tails belong to the mice.

WRITING SKILLS

Underline the possessive noun in the sentence.

1. How many people's homes did you build?
2. All of the men's shirts were gray.

Rewrite the underlined part of the sentence. Use a possessive noun.

3. The dresses of the women are beautiful.

   ____

4. The heels of her feet rubbed against the shoes.

   ____

Try It

More Plural Possessive Nouns

Take Possession

Complete the sentence by making the noun possessive. The first one has been done for you.

1. The ___cattle's___ moos were very loud. (cattle)
2. ________________ books are fun to read! (Children)
3. What color are the ________________ wings? (geese)
4. The ________________ voices boomed. (men)
5. The ________________ tails bounced as they ran. (sheep)
6. Ice cream makes my ________________ roots hurt. (teeth)
7. Skydiving is some ________________ idea of fun. (people)
8. My mom went to an all-________________ school. (women)

WRITING SKILLS

Get Ready

What Is a Book Review?

Pat's Book Review

Use Pat's book review as you work through the lessons in the unit.

Clap Your Hands for Peter Pan

by Pat Stokes

I read a great book. It is called *Peter Pan* by James M. Barrie. The main characters are Wendy, John, and Michael Darling; Peter Pan; Tinker Bell; and Captain Hook. Peter is a boy who never grows up. He knows how to fly. He has a magic fairy called Tinker Bell. Captain Hook is a pirate. The story takes place in the Darling home and Neverland.

Peter shows Wendy, John, and Michael how to fly. They all fly to Neverland. First, they meet the lost boys. The boys ask Wendy to be their mother and tell them stories. The boys tell Wendy about Captain Hook and the crocodile that ate his hand after Peter cut it off. One day, the pirates grab Wendy and the boys. Then, Captain Hook tries to poison Peter. Tinker Bell drinks the poison, but Peter saves her. He asks everyone to clap their

WRITING SKILLS

hands if they believe in fairies. Next, Peter sneaks on the pirate ship and saves Wendy and the boys. He fights with Captain Hook. Hook jumps into the water and is eaten by the crocodile. Peter takes Wendy and the boys home. Mr. and Mrs. Darling adopt the lost boys. But Peter wants to stay in Neverland. He does not want to go to school or grow up. He visits Wendy once a year. Read the book to find out how it ends.

I really liked this book. Peter Pan and Tinker Bell are wonderful characters. The book showed me it would be fun to fly. It also made me think about staying a kid forever. I wouldn't want to be like Peter. I want to be like Wendy and the boys. Then, I could learn to fly and still grow up. I recommend this book because it's a great adventure.

Learn

What Is a Book Review?

The Parts of a Book Review

Guided Exercises

A **book review** tells about a book and gives an opinion about it.

The title of Pat's Book Review is "Clap Your Hands for Peter Pan." It is a book review of the book *Peter Pan.*
What is the name of the author of *Peter Pan*?

WRITING SKILLS

Use Pat's Book Review to answer the questions.

1. What is the setting of the book?

____

2. Who are the main characters in the book?

____

3. Write one event described in the book review.

____

4. Did Pat like the book? How do you know?

____

____

Try It

What Is a Book Review?

Choose Your Book

Use these ideas to help choose a book to review:

- Interesting titles, subjects, and favorite authors
- The summary on the back cover or book flap
- Favorite books of friends, family members, or a librarian
- A new book in a series or about a favorite character

Make a list of books on a separate sheet of paper and choose the book you want to review. Write the title, author, characters, and a reason why you chose the book on this page.

Title ______________________________

Author ______________________________

Characters ______________________________

____

____

My reason for choosing this book ______________________________

____

____

____

Get Ready

Plan a Summary for a Book Review

Pat's Summary Graphic Organizer

Use Pat's graphic organizer as you work through the lessons in the unit.

About the Book

Title: *Peter Pan*

Author: J. M. Barrie

Characters: Wendy, Michael, John Darling; Peter Pan, a boy who never grows up; Tinker Bell, his magic fairy; Captain Hook, a pirate

Setting: Darling home, Neverland

Beginning

Peter shows Wendy, John, and Michael how to fly

Fly to Neverland

Meet lost boys

Wendy plays mother

Wendy tells stories

Lost boys tell about Captain Hook

Crocodile ate his hand

WRITING SKILLS

Middle

Pirates grab Wendy and boys

Hook tries to poison Peter

Tinker Bell drinks poison

Peter saves her

Clap your hands if you believe

Peter saves Wendy and boys

Peter beats Hook

End

Peter takes Wendy and boys home

Lost boys adopted

Peter stays in Neverland

Never grows up

Visits Wendy once a year

Learn

Plan a Summary for a Book Review

What Is a Summary?

Guided Exercises

To **summarize** means to briefly restate the main events of a story in the order in which they happened and without every detail.

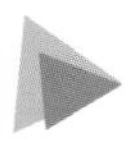

Pat organized the main events in his graphic organizer under "Beginning," "Middle," and "End."

Which event happens first?

WRITING SKILLS

Use Pat's Book Review and Pat's Summary Graphic Organizer to answer the question.

1. Which paragraph in the book review has the events listed in the graphic organizer?

____

Where in the graphic organizer are these events from the book review? Choose the answer.

2. They all fly to Neverland.

   A. Beginning B. Middle C. End

3. Peter fights with Captain Hook.

   A. Beginning B. Middle C. End

4. Mr. and Mrs. Darling adopt the lost boys.

   A. Beginning B. Middle C. End

Try It

Plan a Summary for a Book Review

Summary Graphic Organizer

Write the main events from your book in the order in which they happened.

About the Book

Title:

Author:

Characters:

Setting:

Beginning

Middle

End

WRITING SKILLS

Get Ready

Opinion Statements and Support for a Book Review

Pat's Opinion Statement Graphic Organizer

Use Pat's graphic organizer as you work through the lessons in the unit.

Opinion
like book

Reason
Peter Pan and Tinker Bell

Reason
not growing up

WRITING SKILLS

Learn

Opinion Statements and Support for a Book Review

Opinions and Supporting Evidence

Guided Exercises

An **opinion** tells how you feel about something. It should be supported with reasons.

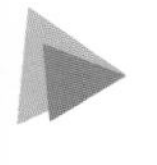

Point to Pat's opinion in Pat's Opinion Statement Graphic Organizer and Pat's Book Review.

Where is Pat's opinion statement in the book review?

Use Pat's Book Review and Pat's Opinion Statement Graphic Organizer to answer the questions.

1. What is Pat's opinion statement?

____

2. What sentence tells Pat's first supporting reason?

____

____

3. What sentence tells Pat's second supporting reason?

____

____

WRITING SKILLS

Try It

Opinion Statements and Support for a Book Review

Opinion Statement Graphic Organizer

Use the graphic organizer to write an opinion and two reasons for your feeling about your book.

Opinion

Reason

Reason

WRITING SKILLS

Learn

Draft a Book Review

Write a Concluding Sentence

Guided Exercises

A **concluding sentence** in a book review includes a recommendation for the reader.

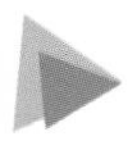

In the concluding sentence of Pat's Book Review, Pat wrote a recommendation for readers.

- Where is Pat's concluding statement?
- What is Pat's reason for recommending the book?

Write a concluding sentence for your book review. Be sure to include a reason why you do or do not recommend the book.

____

____

____

____

____

____

Try It

Draft a Book Review

Draft Your Book Review

Use your Summary Graphic Organizer and Opinion Statement Graphic Organizer to help you write your book review. Use additional sheets of paper if you need more room.

- In your first paragraph, tell about your book.
- In your second paragraph, summarize the main events.
- In your conclusion, state your opinion, two reasons, and your recommendation.

WRITING SKILLS

Write a Book Review

Book Review Checklist

Use this checklist as you work through the book review in the lesson.

☐ Did I include all the parts of a book review?

- Introductory sentence
- Title
- Author
- Characters
- Setting
- Summary of events
- My opinion
- Supporting reasons
- Recommendation

☐ Do I have three paragraphs?

- Paragraph 1: Introduce the book
- Paragraph 2: Summarize the book
- Paragraph 3: Conclude with opinion, reasons, and concluding sentence

☐ Did I support my main idea with details?

☐ Are my sentences complete?

WRITING SKILLS

- [ ] Are apostrophes used correctly in contractions and possessives?
- [ ] Did I use nouns, pronouns, verbs, and adjectives correctly?
- [ ] Did I use transition words?
- [ ] Do my sentences show variety?
- [ ] Did I capitalize proper nouns and the first word in a sentence?
- [ ] Did I use a dictionary to check my spelling?

Write Now

Write a Book Review

Revise, Proofread, and Publish a Book Review

Use the Book Review Checklist to revise and proofread your book review. Then, write a clean, final copy of your review.

WRITING SKILLS

Learn

Names and Initials of People

Capital Ideas

Guided Exercises

Use a capital letter to begin a name. Use a capital letter for an initial and add a period.

Sally Ride was an astronaut.

The proper noun is underlined. Circle the capital letters.

S. R. are Sally Ride's initials.

Underline the initials in the sentence. Circle the periods in the initials.

Write the name correctly. Then, write the person's initials.

Incorrect Name	Correct Name	Initials
1. liz chu		
2. thomas jobs		
3. donna fields		
4. harry gray		
5. ana lee carr		

WRITING SKILLS

Try It

Names and Initials of People

Famous American Names and Initials

Write the name of the underlined person correctly.

1. george washington is "the Father of Our Country."

   ____

2. Yet, the Declaration of Independence was written by thomas jefferson.

   ____

Write the initials of the underlined name.

3. John Adams signed the Declaration of Independence.

   ____

4. John Adams wrote many letters to his wife, Abigail Adams.

   ____

5. John and Abigail Adams had a son named John Quincy Adams.

   ____

Get Ready

Titles of People

Titles and Their Abbreviations

We call some people by both their names and their titles. Many titles can be shortened or abbreviated. Here are some common titles and their abbreviations:

Title	Abbreviation
Mister	Mr.
Mistress	Mrs. (pronounced ***MIH-suhz***)
Miss or Mistress	Ms. (pronounced ***mihz***)
Doctor	Dr.
Reverend	Rev.
Captain	Capt.
General	Gen.
Governor	Gov.

Notice that ***Ms.*** can be used as a shortened form of ***Miss*** or ***Mistress***.

WRITING SKILLS

Learn

Titles of People

Titles Aren't Just for Books

Guided Exercises

Use a capital letter to begin a person's title. A shortened title is followed by a period.

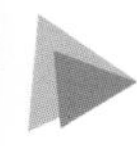

Who lives next to Doctor Shaw?

The title is underlined. Circle the capital letter in the title.

Who lives next to Dr. Shaw?

Underline the shortened title. Circle the period.

WRITING SKILLS

Use capital letters and periods correctly to write the underlined words.

1. I went to see mrs. Lewis. ____________________
2. Then, I ran into mister Rose. ____________________
3. They had seen dr Greene. ____________________

Choose the correct shortened form of the title.

4. Governor

   A. Gov B. Gvnr. C. gover D. Gov.

5. Captain

   A. Capt. B. capt. C. Cn. D. Capt

Try It

Titles of People

Title Town

Use capital letters and periods correctly to write the underlined words.

1. Today, mr. Garcia swept his porch. ____________________

2. He saw miss Faye on the sidewalk. ____________________

3. She was with uncle Al. ____________________

4. They were going to meet rev Mann. ____________________

5. mrs Jackson said she was going, too. ____________________

6. She had seen dr patel drive toward the clinic. ____________________

Choose the answer.

7. Which sentence is **not** written correctly?
   - **A.** The troops were led by Gen. Long.
   - **B.** The bill was signed by Gov. Post.
   - **C.** The hero was Capt. Norman.
   - **D.** Ms Jones marched in the parade.

WRITING SKILLS

Learn

Place Names

Place It Here

Guided Exercises

Use a capital letter to begin the name of a town, a city, a state, or a country.

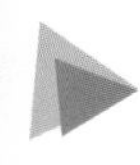

The biggest city in England is London.

The proper nouns are underlined. Circle the capital letters.

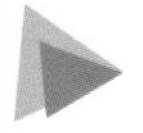

My cousin lives in Austin, Texas.

Underline the proper nouns. Circle the capital letters.

Find the word or words that are written incorrectly. Use capital letters to write the name or names correctly.

1. Did you ever visit the state of california? ____________________
2. I just went to sacramento, which is the capital city. __________
3. It is not as big as the city of los angeles. ____________________
4. It isn't as cool as the city of san francisco. ____________________
5. Yet, I like it better than portland, oregon. ____________________
6. I also like it better than my town of weston. ________________

WRITING SKILLS

Try It

Place Names

Your Turn

Capitalize the place name or names in the sentence correctly.

1. I'm thinking of a place in the country of italy.

   ____

2. But, I'm not thinking of rome, which is a very old city.

   ____

3. I'm not thinking of casoli, either, which is my grandmother's hometown.

   ____

4. The city is closer to the country of france.

   ____

5. It isn't venice, though, which is a city full of canals.

   ____

6. It is the city of pisa, which has a famous leaning tower.

   ____

WRITING SKILLS

Get Ready

What Is a Presentation?

Presentation Skills

Use this list of presentation skills as you work through the lessons in the unit.

- Be creative when you do your presentation.
- Start with a sentence or question.
- Read the review slowly and clearly.
- Speak at an appropriate pace.
- Use a friendly voice and speak loudly.
- Speak with enthusiasm and expression.
- Look up at your audience as much as possible.
- Include something for the audience to look at.
- Ask the audience questions during the presentation.
- Have the audience ask you questions.
- Talk to the audience about the book.
- Express your opinion and support it with reasons.
- Make a recommendation about the book.
- Practice the presentation so you know what to say.

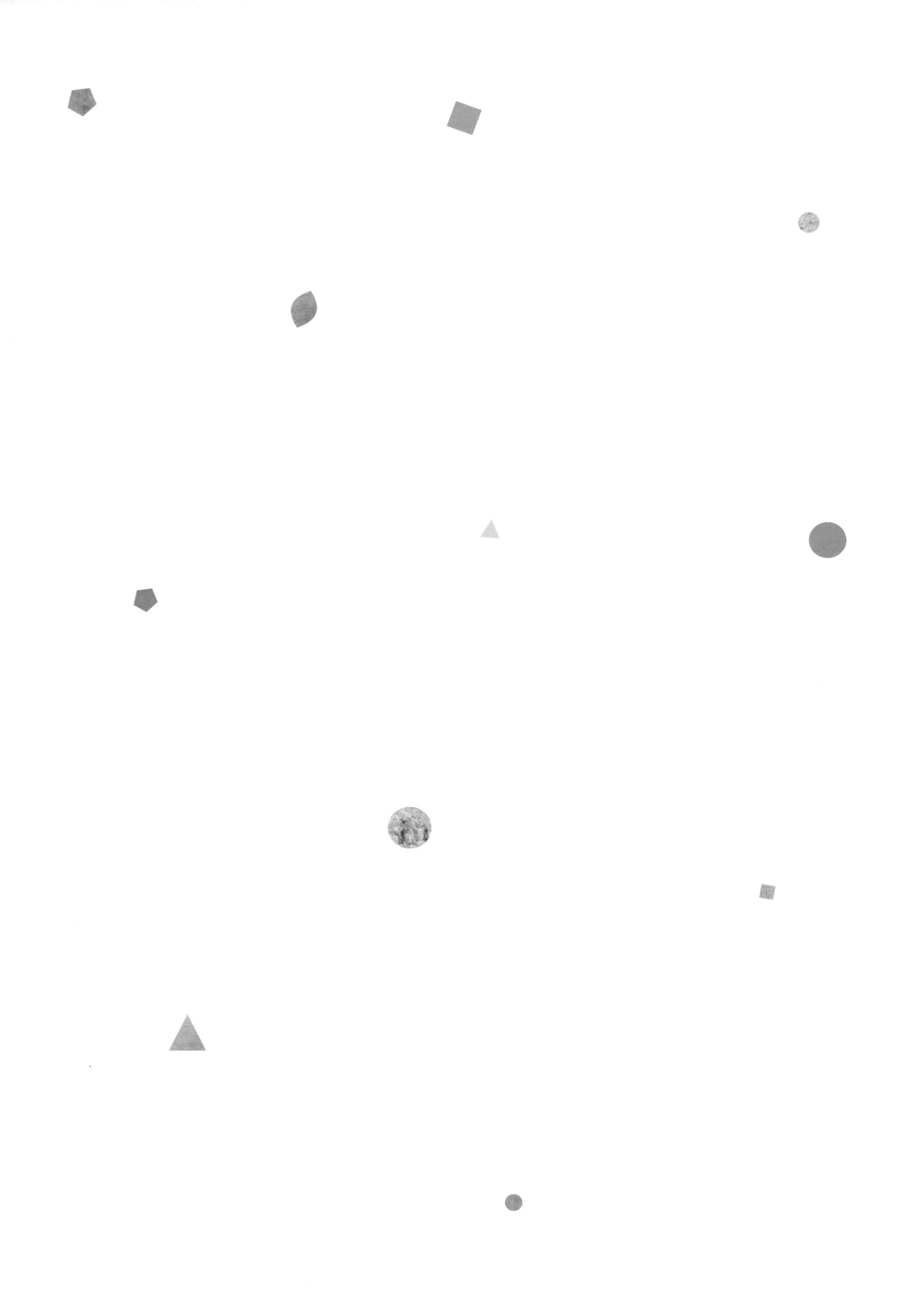

Learn

Create a Visual

How to Create a Visual

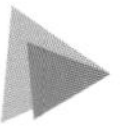

Guided Exercises

A **visual** is a graphic, picture, chart, or photograph. It has a purpose.

Pat's presentation had two visuals.

- What visuals did Pat use?
- What was the purpose of the visuals?

Use these ideas for choosing a visual.

- Drawings, illustrations, photos
- Posters, charts, diagrams, maps
- Puppets
- A shoe box that shows a scene or setting from the story
- Costumes or items from the story
- A mobile with cut-out pictures tied to it
- A mini-book with drawings that retell the story

Add your own ideas here ______________________________

____

Try It

Create a Visual

Create!

Choose a visual to go with your book review presentation. Describe the visual. Gather all the materials and start creating the visual.

My visual ______________________________

Purpose of the visual ______________________________

____

Materials ______________________________

____

____

____

____

WRITING SKILLS

Learn

Develop a Presentation

How to Be a Good Speaker

Guided Exercises

Being a good speaker requires planning; clarity of thought; and a strong beginning, middle, and end to your speech.

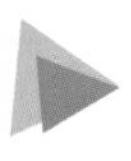

"Peter Pan: by Terry Taylor."

Does this sentence get your attention?

Answer the questions about Terry's presentation.

1. Is Terry's presentation creative and interesting? Why or why not?

____

____

2. List ways Terry can make her presentation more interesting and how she can be a better speaker.

____

____

____

____

WRITING SKILLS

Try It

Develop a Presentation

Work on Your Presentation

Plan your presentation. Decide how you will introduce and end your presentation. Jot down notes to yourself about when to look up or show your visual. Work on your visual.

Introduction ____

____

Conclusion ____

____

Notes to myself ____

____

____

____

____

____

____

WRITING SKILLS

Learn

Practice a Presentation

Listen to Yourself

Guided Exercises

Practicing a presentation will help you look and sound better.

Look up while practicing your presentation to practice speaking to an audience.

Why should you practice with your visual?

WRITING SKILLS

Practice your presentation. Then, use the questions to think about how you did. Practice again. Work on the parts of your presentation that could use improvement.

1. Did you look up? About how many times?

____

2. Did you lose your place? How can you keep that from happening?

____

3. How long was your presentation? Did you speak too slowly or too quickly?

____

4. Does your visual make sense? Do you need to say more about it and its purpose?

____

Try It

Practice a Presentation

Practice Your Presentation

Practice your presentation again. Look for ways to make it better. Think about how you look and sound. Find ways to make it flow smoothly.

Things I do well ________________________________

____

____

Things I can do better ____________________________

____

____

Things I want to change or add ____________________

____

____

____

____

WRITING SKILLS

Write Now

Deliver a Presentation

Time to Present!

After you deliver your book review presentation, use these feedback questions to discuss your presentation with others.

- [ ] Did I speak loudly and clearly?
- [ ] Did I make eye contact with the audience?
- [ ] Did I speak smoothly and sound prepared?
- [ ] Did I have an introduction and a conclusion?
- [ ] Did I present my ideas in the correct order?
- [ ] Did I have a visual? Did I show it at the proper time? Did it connect to my presentation?
- [ ] Did I speak with enthusiasm?
- [ ] Did I include the audience in the presentation?
- [ ] How could the presentation be improved?

____

____

WRITING SKILLS

Peer Interaction

Deliver a Presentation

Tell Me About My Presentation

Have another person answer these questions so you can receive feedback on the presentation you gave.

1. Did the presenter speak loudly and clearly?

   ____

2. Did the presenter make eye contact with the audience?

   ____

3. Did the presenter speak smoothly and sound prepared?

   ____

4. Did the presenter have an introduction and a conclusion?

   ____

5. Did the presenter deliver ideas in the correct order?

   ____

6. Did the presenter have a visual? Did the presenter show it at the proper time? Did it connect to the presentation?

   ____

   ____

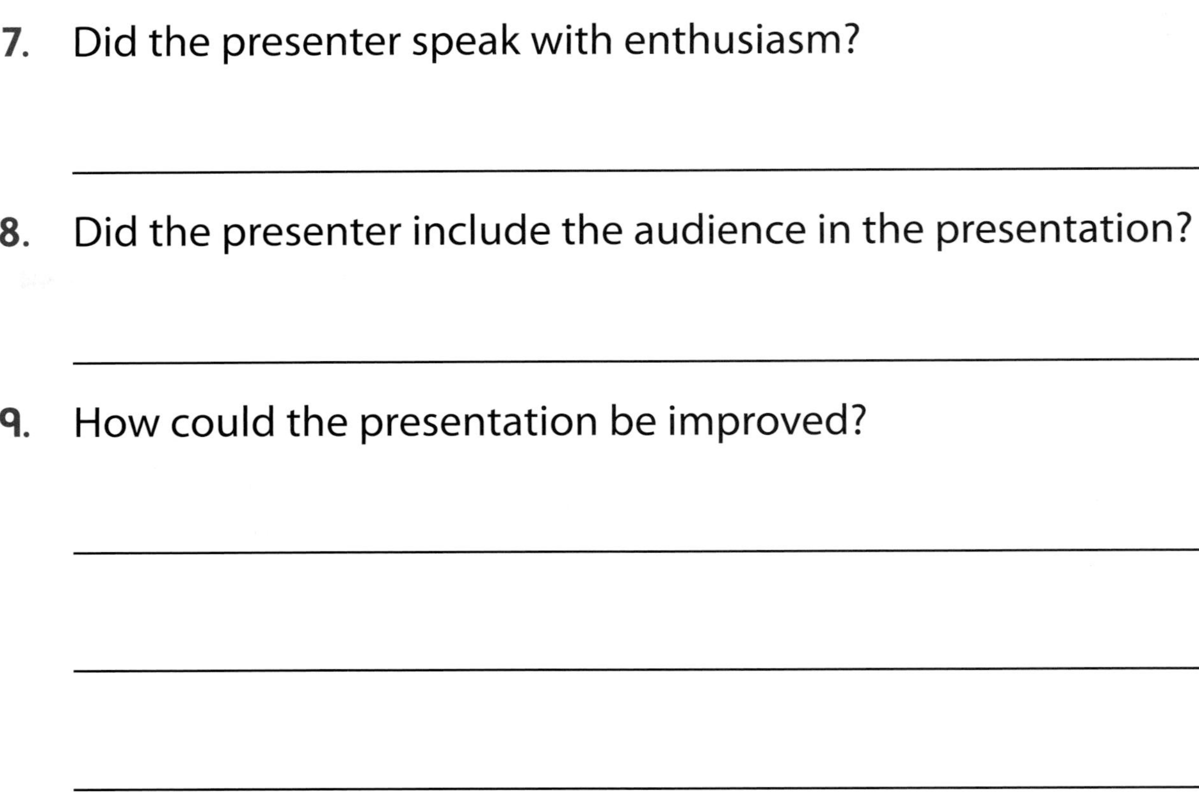

7. Did the presenter speak with enthusiasm?

8. Did the presenter include the audience in the presentation?

9. How could the presentation be improved?

WRITING SKILLS

Learn

Words in a Series

More Uses for Commas

Guided Exercises

Use commas between words in a list or group.

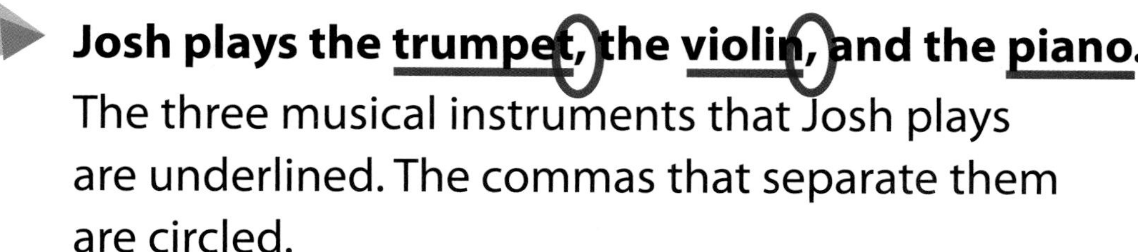

Josh plays the trumpet, the violin, and the piano.

The three musical instruments that Josh plays are underlined. The commas that separate them are circled.

Vickie has a dog a cat and a bird.

Underline the three pets in the sentence. Place commas where they belong.

Place commas where they belong in the sentence.

1. It was a cold windy and snowy day.
2. The movie theater was big crowded and warm.
3. The movie we saw was long boring and silly.
4. Lou Sally and Rich wanted to leave.
5. But, I had popcorn candy and peanuts to eat!

WRITING SKILLS

Try It

Words in a Series

Lists, Lists, Lists

Place commas where they belong.

1. Who ordered the pizza with mushrooms onions and sausage?

2. Mom Dad Aunt Milly and Uncle Ed don't like mushrooms.

3. I'll get some turkey cheese and mustard for sandwiches.

Choose three words from the word bank and finish the sentence.

a hat	February	January
December	boots	gloves

4. The best months to go skiing are ______________________________

____.

5. Of course, you have to wear ______________________________

____.

WRITING SKILLS

Get Ready

Contractions

Contractions with *Not*

A contraction is a shortened form of two words. An apostrophe replaces a missing letter or letters. Many contractions combine a verb and the word *not*.

Two Words	Contraction
is not	isn't
are not	aren't
was not	wasn't
were not	weren't
does not	doesn't
do not	don't
did not	didn't
has not	hasn't
have not	haven't
had not	hadn't
will not	won't
cannot	can't
could not	couldn't
would not	wouldn't
should not	shouldn't

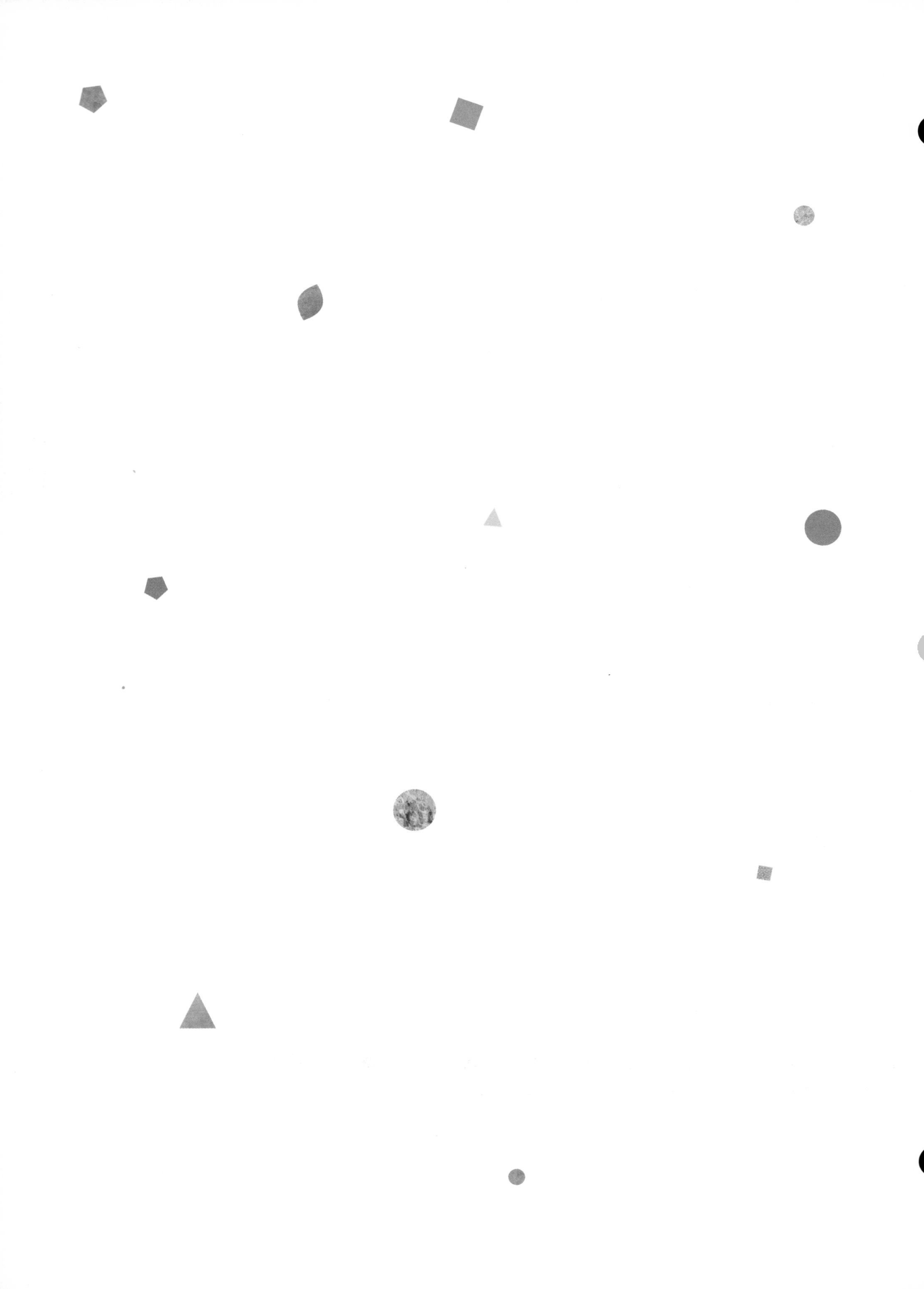

Learn

Contractions

Short Forms

Guided Exercises

A contraction combines two words. An apostrophe replaces the missing letters.

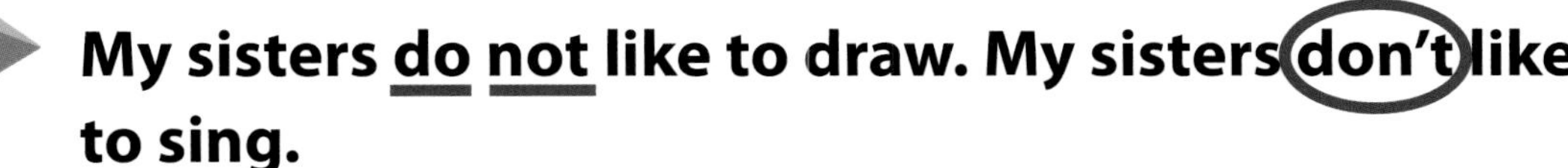

My sisters do not like to draw. My sisters don't like to sing.

The words *do not* are underlined in the first sentence. The contraction for *do not* is circled in the second sentence.

My brothers were not at the game. My brothers weren't ready on time.

Read the sentences. Circle the word that is a contraction for the underlined words in the first sentence.

WRITING SKILLS

Match the underlined words with the correct contraction.

1.	Kim does not have your watch.	didn't
2.	Her friends do not have it.	doesn't
3.	They did not ever see it.	don't

Write a sentence about something you will not do. Use the contraction for *will not* in your sentence.

4. ____

Try It

Contractions

Contraction Action

Complete the sentence by writing the contraction for the words.

1. Bill ________________ see anything. (could not)
2. He knew he ________________ keep going. (should not)
3. If he got lost, he ________________ be able to find his way out of the cave. (would not)
4. Yet, he ________________ stop. (did not)
5. "I ________________ leave this cave without the treasure," Bill said. (will not)
6. "Are you telling me you ________________ scared?" Lisa asked. (are not)
7. "It ________________ that," Bill replied. (is not)
8. "It just ________________ make sense to quit." (does not)
9. "I ________________ given up hope yet." (have not)
10. "You ________________ keep going," Lisa said. (cannot)

WRITING SKILLS

Get Ready

More Contractions

Two Become One

A contraction is a shortened form of two words. An apostrophe replaces a missing letter or letters. Many contractions combine a pronoun and a verb.

Two Words	Contraction
I am	I'm
you are	you're
he is	he's
she is	she's
it is	it's
we are	we're
they are	they're
I will	I'll
you will	you'll
he will	he'll
she will	she'll
it will	it'll
we will	we'll
they will	they'll
that is	that's

Learn

More Contractions

Contraction Crazy

Guided Exercises

Many contractions are made up of a pronoun and a verb.

We are very happy. We're happy we won the game.

The words *we are* are underlined in the first sentence. The contraction for *we are* is circled in the second sentence.

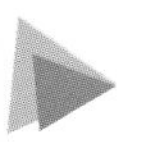

You will watch the game next time. You'll see us play a good team.

Read the sentences. Circle the word that is a contraction for the underlined words in the first sentence.

WRITING SKILLS

Match the underlined words with the correct contraction.

1. It is raining today. — I'm
2. I am going to read my new book. — It's
3. I know I will enjoy it. — I'll

Answer the question in a sentence. Use a contraction that has the word *she* in your answer.

4. What is she going to do now?

____

Try It

More Contractions

Contractions for All

Complete the sentence by writing the contraction for the words.

1. Linda said, "__________ get my coat." (I will)

2. "__________ not that cold," I told her. (It is)

3. "Well, __________ from Canada," she replied. (you are)

4. I laughed and said, " __________ true." (That is)

5. Linda joked that __________ like a polar bear. (I am)

6. "__________ always warm in January," she said to Amy. (He is)

7. I said, "And, __________ cold in July." (she is)

8. "Then, I think __________ need a coat," Amy said with a smile. (you will)

Choose the correct contraction for the underlined words.

9. <u>We will</u> wait near the swings.

   A. We're

   B. Well

   C. We'll

   D. W'ell

WRITING SKILLS

What Is Research?

Evan's Report

Evan published a report on Helen Keller. Use Evan's report as you work through the lessons in the unit.

A Remarkable Woman

Helen Keller was an amazing person. She was born in Alabama in 1880. She was a healthy child. Then, she got sick. She lost her sight and her hearing. She did not know how to talk with her family. When she was seven, a teacher came to her home. The teacher's name was Anne Sullivan. She made Helen understand what water was. One word changed Helen's life.

Helen learned many words after that. She learned how to communicate with others. She went to college with Anne's help. Helen and Anne stayed friends for the rest of their lives. Helen became a writer. She used a typewriter made for blind people. She traveled all over the world. Helen tried to help other blind and deaf people. She was also interested in women's rights. Helen won the Medal of Freedom. Helen was a very special person.

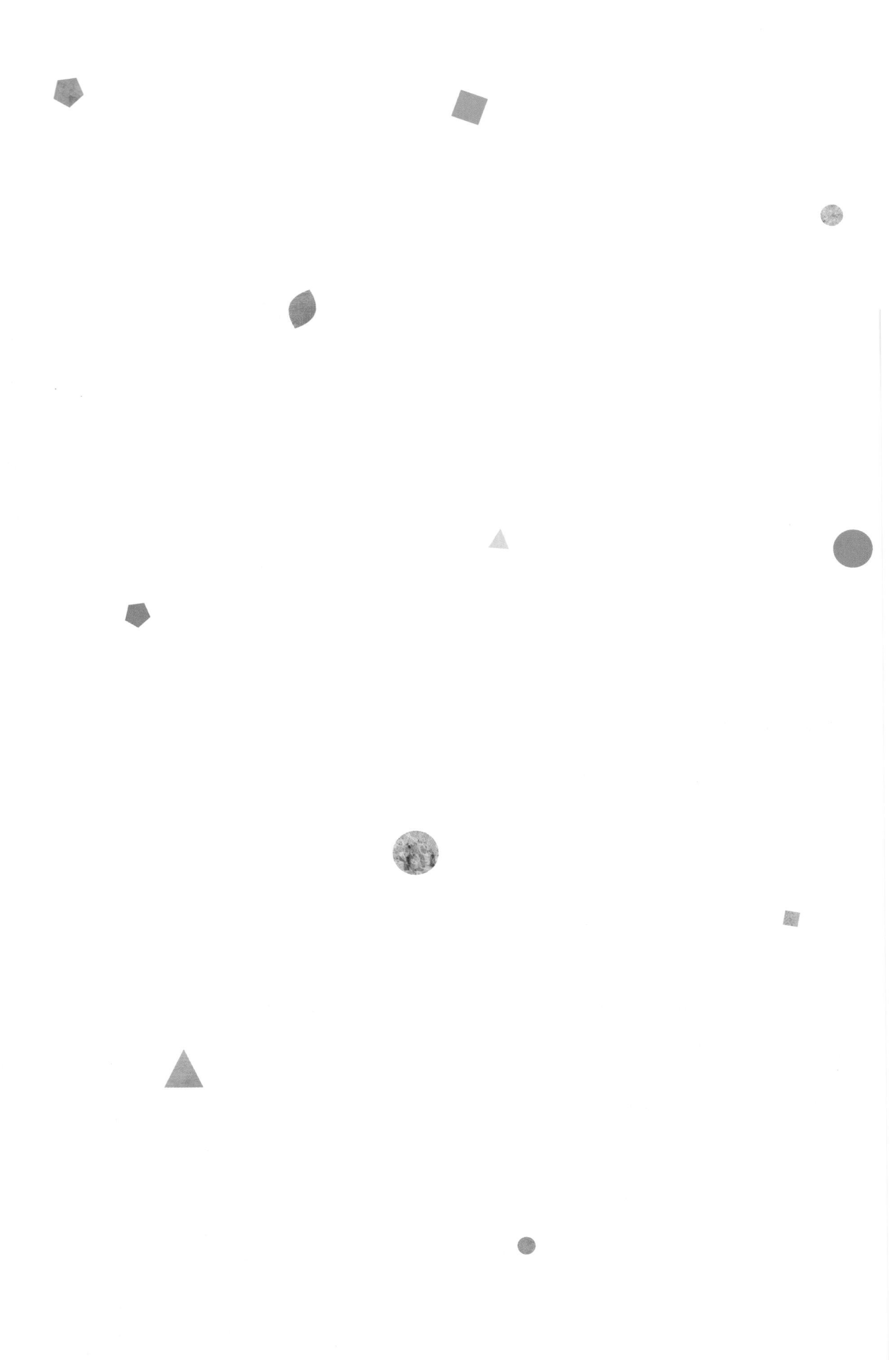

Learn

What Is Research?

Explain Research

Guided Exercises

Research means looking up facts and information.

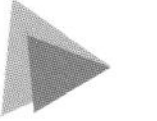

Evan did research about Helen Keller. Here is a fact he found.

She was born in Alabama in 1880.

Find two other facts in Evan's first paragraph.

Read Evan's Report and choose the answer.

1. Which of these statements is Evan's opinion?
   - **A.** Helen never married.
   - **B.** Helen was an interesting person.
   - **C.** Helen used a typewriter made for blind people.
   - **D.** Helen won the Medal of Freedom.

2. What information did the parents in Evan's audience probably already know?
   - **A.** who Helen Keller was
   - **B.** that Helen Keller died in 1968
   - **C.** why Helen Keller lost her sight and hearing
   - **D.** that Helen Keller won the Medal of Freedom

WRITING SKILLS

What Is Research?

Ask Questions on a Topic

Choose a topic from your brainstorming list. Pick a person, an event, or an animal you would like to learn more about. Write your topic on the line. Then, write what you know about your topic in the first column. Write at least three questions about what you want to know in the other column.

WRITING SKILLS

Topic ______________________________

What I Know	What I Wonder

Get Ready

References

Where Do You Find Information?

Use this list of references as you work through the lessons in the unit.

almanac a book that comes out every year with facts on many topics

atlas a book of maps

diary a personal account of things that happen every day; most diaries are private, but some diaries of famous people have been published

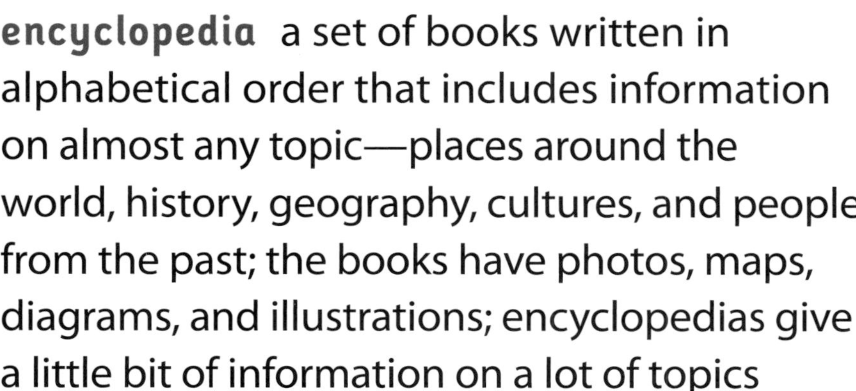

encyclopedia a set of books written in alphabetical order that includes information on almost any topic—places around the world, history, geography, cultures, and people from the past; the books have photos, maps, diagrams, and illustrations; encyclopedias give a little bit of information on a lot of topics

interview one person asking another person questions; you can read or watch interviews done by someone else, or you can do your own interviews, talking to people you know or people who know something about your topic

letter a message sent from one person to another; sometimes letters by famous people are published; you can also find information by writing to experts and reading the letters they write back to you

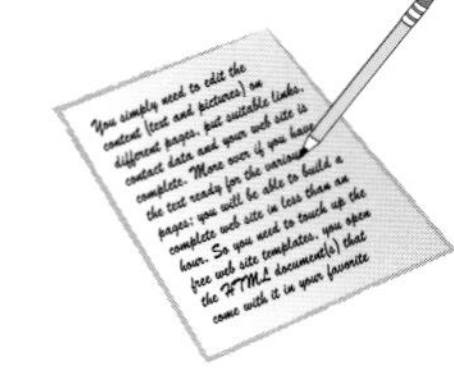

magazine a publication on many different topics that includes articles and interviews that are mostly about things happening now

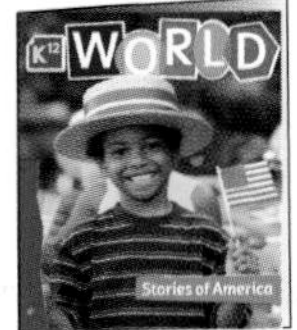

nonfiction book a book on a specific topic that includes facts, details, time lines, and often photos

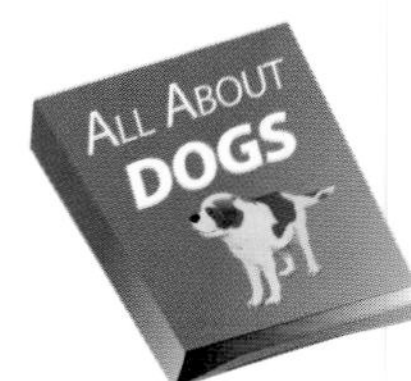

website an address on the Internet that has information on a topic, person, or place

Learn

References

Where Would You Look?

Guided Exercises

A **reference** is a work that contains useful information for a writer, such as an encyclopedia, a dictionary, or a website.

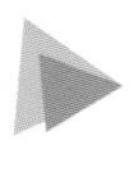

Evan used an encyclopedia to start his research and a second reference to write his report.

Which would have been more useful for writing a report on Helen Keller—a biography of Helen Keller or a women's magazine?

WRITING SKILLS

Choose the answer.

1. Which of these references would have given Evan the most information about Helen Keller?

   A. *The Story of My Life* by Helen Keller

   B. an almanac

   C. an atlas

   D. an encyclopedia

2. Which of these references would **not** have provided useful information on Helen Keller?

   A. the Internet

   B. an atlas

   C. an encyclopedia

   D. a nonfiction book

Try It

References

Reference Materials

Find reference materials for your topic. Use at least two different references to write your report, such as a book and an Internet site or an encyclopedia. Write the name of the reference and the What I Wonder questions that you think it will answer. If you think the reference will answer new questions, write them, too.

Reference ____

What I Wonder ____

____

____

Reference ____

What I Wonder ____

____

____

WRITING SKILLS

Get Ready

Take Notes (A)

Evan's Note Card

Use Evan's Note Card as you work through the lessons in the unit.

What I Wonder

What happened to Helen as a child?

Fact	Reference
became deaf and blind when she was little	*The Life of Helen Keller*

Learn

Take Notes (A)

How Do You Take Notes?

Guided Exercises

To **take notes** means to find facts and important information, and rewrite them in your own words.

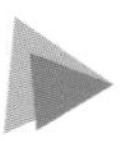

Evan wondered how Helen communicated with others. He learned that Anne spelled words in Helen's hand.

- Is this fact important?
- Circle the words that Evan needs to write under Fact on his note card.

Use this information to fill in the note card: Evan wondered why Helen was famous. He read *The Life of Helen Keller*. He learned that Helen was the author of a dozen books.

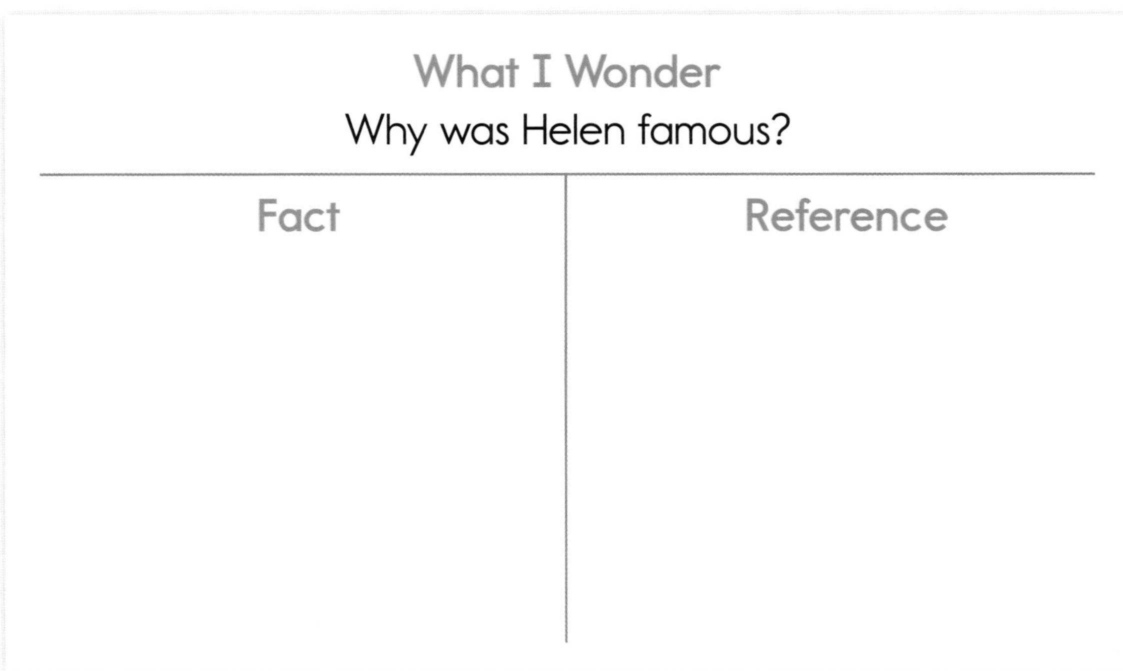

WRITING SKILLS

Try It

Take Notes (A)

Write Your Notes

Write each What I Wonder question on a separate card. Read your references and take notes on your questions. You should write more than one fact on a card, but all facts on a card should answer the What I Wonder question.

What I Wonder	
Fact	**Reference**

What I Wonder	
Fact	**Reference**

WRITING SKILLS

Learn

Take Notes (B)

In Your Own Words

Guided Exercises

Find the important information and write it in your own words. Don't copy someone else's words.

"Helen was intelligent and had an amazing memory."

- Circle the important ideas.
- Evan wrote on his note card: "Helen was smart and had a great memory." Did Evan write the note in his own words?

WRITING SKILLS

Circle the sentence that does not copy the sentence shown.

1. Bats hang from trees, roofs, bridges, and caves.
   A. Bats hang from roofs, caves, trees, and bridges.
   B. Bats like to hang from things.

2. Bats eat nectar from flowers, fruit, fish or insects.
   A. Bats eat different kinds of food.
   B. Bats eat fruit, fish, flowers, and insects.

Write in your own words: "Bats fly, but they are not birds."

3. ______________________________

Try It

Take Notes (B)

Finish Your Notes

Finish taking notes as you read your reference materials. Complete your other cards or start new ones. Be sure to put all facts in your own words.

What I Wonder

Fact	Reference

What I Wonder

Fact	Reference

WRITING SKILLS

Get Ready

Create a Plan

Evan's Outline

Use Evan's outline as you work through the lessons in the unit.

Subject Helen Keller

Body Paragraph 1

Main Topic (What I Wonder) What was Helen like as a child?

Facts became deaf and blind
could not talk with family

Main Idea Helen could not understand

WRITING SKILLS

Learn

Create a Plan

How to Organize

Guided Exercises

An **outline** organizes information. You can create a plan by reviewing your facts and finding the main idea that holds them together.

Helen could not understand.

- This is the main idea of Evan's first paragraph.
- What are the two facts in the outline that support the main idea?

Use Evan's Report to fill in the second half of his outline.

Body Paragraph 2

Main Topic (What I Wonder) ____________________

____

Facts ____________________

____

Main Idea ____________________

____

WRITING SKILLS

Try It

Create a Plan

Organize Your Information

Fill in your outline. Organize information in an order that makes sense.

Introduce Subject ______________________________

Body Paragraph 1

Main Topic (What I Wonder) ______________________________

Facts ______________________________

____

____

Main Idea ______________________________

Body Paragraph 2

Main Topic (What I Wonder) ______________________________

Facts ______________________________

____

____

Main Idea ______________________________

WRITING SKILLS

Learn

Months and Days

On the Calendar

WRITING SKILLS

Guided Exercises

Use a capital letter to begin the name of a month and the name of a day.

The underlined words are proper nouns. They were missing capital letters. The capital letters were added.

The next game is on friday.

Underline the proper noun. Draw a line (/) through the small letter. Write the capital letter above it.

Underline the word that needs a capital letter. Draw a line (/) through the small letter. Write the capital letter above it.

1. April showers bring may flowers.

2. I will pay you on tuesday.

3. We have pizza every sunday night.

4. Is july the hottest month?

5. The longest day of the year is in june.

Try It

Months and Days

Which Day or Month?

WRITING SKILLS

Choose the sentence that uses capital letters correctly.

1. Which sentence is written correctly?
   - **A.** The Day after sunday is monday.
   - **B.** The day after Sunday is monday.
   - **C.** The day after Sunday is Monday.

2. Which sentence is written correctly?
   - **A.** The last month of the Year is december.
   - **B.** The last month of the year is December.
   - **C.** The last Month of the year is December.

3. Which sentence is written correctly?
   - **A.** The only day that begins with *w* is Wednesday.
   - **B.** The only Day that begins with *w* is wednesday.
   - **C.** The only day that begins with *w* is wednesday.

Finish the sentence.

4. My favorite month is ______________________________.

5. My favorite day of the week is ______________________.

Learn

Holidays

Happy Holidays

Guided Exercises

Use a capital letter to begin each word in the name of a holiday.

The name of the holiday is underlined. It was missing capital letters. The capital letters were added.

Our summer vacation ended on labor day.

Underline the name of the holiday. Draw a line (/) through the small letters. Write the capital letters above them.

WRITING SKILLS

Underline the words that need capital letters. Draw lines through the small letters. Write the capital letters above them.

1. We saw my grandfather on new year's day.

2. He sent me roses on valentine's day.

3. On st. patrick's day, he made me green pancakes.

4. He promised that we would go fishing on memorial day.

Try It

Holidays

Capitals for Holidays

Choose the holiday that completes the sentence. Write it on the line. Remember to use capital letters correctly.

presidents' day	mother's day	halloween
april fool's day	father's day	labor day

1. Children can dress in costumes and get lots of candy on

   ______________________________.

2. George Washington is remembered on a holiday called

   ______________________________.

3. Jane played a funny trick on ______________________________.

4. I gave my dad a tie for ______________________________.

5. Mothers are honored on ______________________________.

Finish the sentence.

6. My favorite holiday is ______________________________.

Learn

Product Names and More

Guided Exercises

Use capital letters to begin the brand names of products.

Our new car is an Edgemont.
The product name is underlined in the sentence.
The capital letter is circled.

The edgemont is red, and we bought it on monday.
Draw a line through each small letter that should be a capital letter. Write the capital letter above it.

Read the letter. Draw a line through each small letter that should be a capital letter. Write the capital letter above it.

dear Mr. Rose,

I am writing to you because i have a problem. you see, I always wear coolster brand jeans. However, a pair of my jeans ripped in the wash on thursday. So, I want my money back.

sincerely,

Gina Williams

WRITING SKILLS

Try It

Product Names and More

Practice with Capital Letters

Choose the answer.

1. Which greeting uses capital letters correctly?

   A. Dear jason, **B.** dear jason, **C.** Dear Jason,

2. Which closing uses capital letters correctly?

   A. yours Truly, **B.** Yours truly, **C.** yours truly,

3. Which sentence uses capital letters correctly?

   A. My mom and I have brown hair.

   B. My mom and i have brown hair.

   C. my mom and I have brown hair.

4. Which sentence uses capital letters correctly?

   A. Is that a fittz shirt?

   B. Is that a Fittz shirt?

   C. Is that a fittz Shirt?

Write a sentence about your favorite cereal.

5. ____

   ____

WRITING SKILLS

Organize Your Paragraphs

Lily's Report

Lily published a report on the diplodocus. Use Lily's report as you work through the lessons in the unit.

Diplodocus ← **Title**

Lily Chen

If you like the *Land Before Time* movies, you might know who Doc is. He was a long-necked dinosaur. In fact, he was a diplodocus. What did he look like? ← **Introduction**

A diplodocus is one of the longest dinosaurs. It had a very long neck and a very small head. Its teeth were shaped like pencils. It had a long tail. The tail could swing back and forth. This helped save it from enemies. The dinosaur walked on all four legs. It walked slowly. ← **Body Paragraph 1**

The diplodocus lived in the Jurassic Period. It lived on land with apatosaurus and stegosaurus. Fossils were found in the Rocky Mountains, Colorado, Montana, Utah, and Wyoming. Diplodocus ate plants. Another name for that is herbivore. It did not chew the plants. Instead, it ate them whole. Also, it stood on its back legs and ate tall plants. ← **Body Paragraph 2**

Dinosaurs are fun to read about. Diplodocus is one of the most interesting of all. ← **Conclusion**

Learn

Organize Your Paragraphs

Organize Thoughts and Facts

Guided Exercises

Organize paragraphs so each is about a main idea. Organize facts in the paragraphs by time, importance, or logical order.

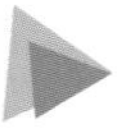

Lily organized her report.

- How are the paragraphs organized?
- How are the facts inside the paragraphs organized?

WRITING SKILLS

Lily has more facts in her notes. Where does each fact belong?

1. It ate a lot of food. Body Paragraph 1
2. It was 90 feet long. Body Paragraph 2
3. It has a funny name. Doesn't Belong
4. Where does this fact belong in Lily's Body Paragraph 1?
   It was one of the slowest dinosaurs.
   - **A.** Beginning
   - **B.** Middle
   - **C.** End

Try It

Organize Your Paragraphs

Create Order

Choose the best order for your report. Check paragraphs 1 and 2. Then, rewrite the facts in your outline in the correct order.

1. What is the main idea of each of your paragraphs? Write one main idea on each line.

   ____

   ____

2. Check the order of your paragraphs. Are they in an order that makes sense?

   A. Yes　　**B.** No

3. If you answered No, reorder your paragraphs on your original outline or on a separate sheet of paper.

4. Review your facts within your paragraphs. How should they be organized? (time order, order of importance, or logical order)

   ____

5. Rewrite your outline in correct order.

WRITING SKILLS

Get Ready

Write the Body (A)

Lily's Outline

Use Lily's Outline as you work through the lessons in the unit.

Subject Diplodocus

Title Diplodocus

Introduction *Land Before Time*

Body Paragraph 1

What did it look like?

Fact 1: long neck

Fact 2: swinging tail

Fact 3: walked slowly

Main Idea was very long

Body Paragraph 2

Where did it live and what did it eat?

Fact 1: Jurassic Period

Fact 2: lived Rocky Mountains

Fact 3: didn't chew the plants

Fact 4: ate tall plants

Main Idea lived on land and ate plants

Conclusion most interesting dinosaur

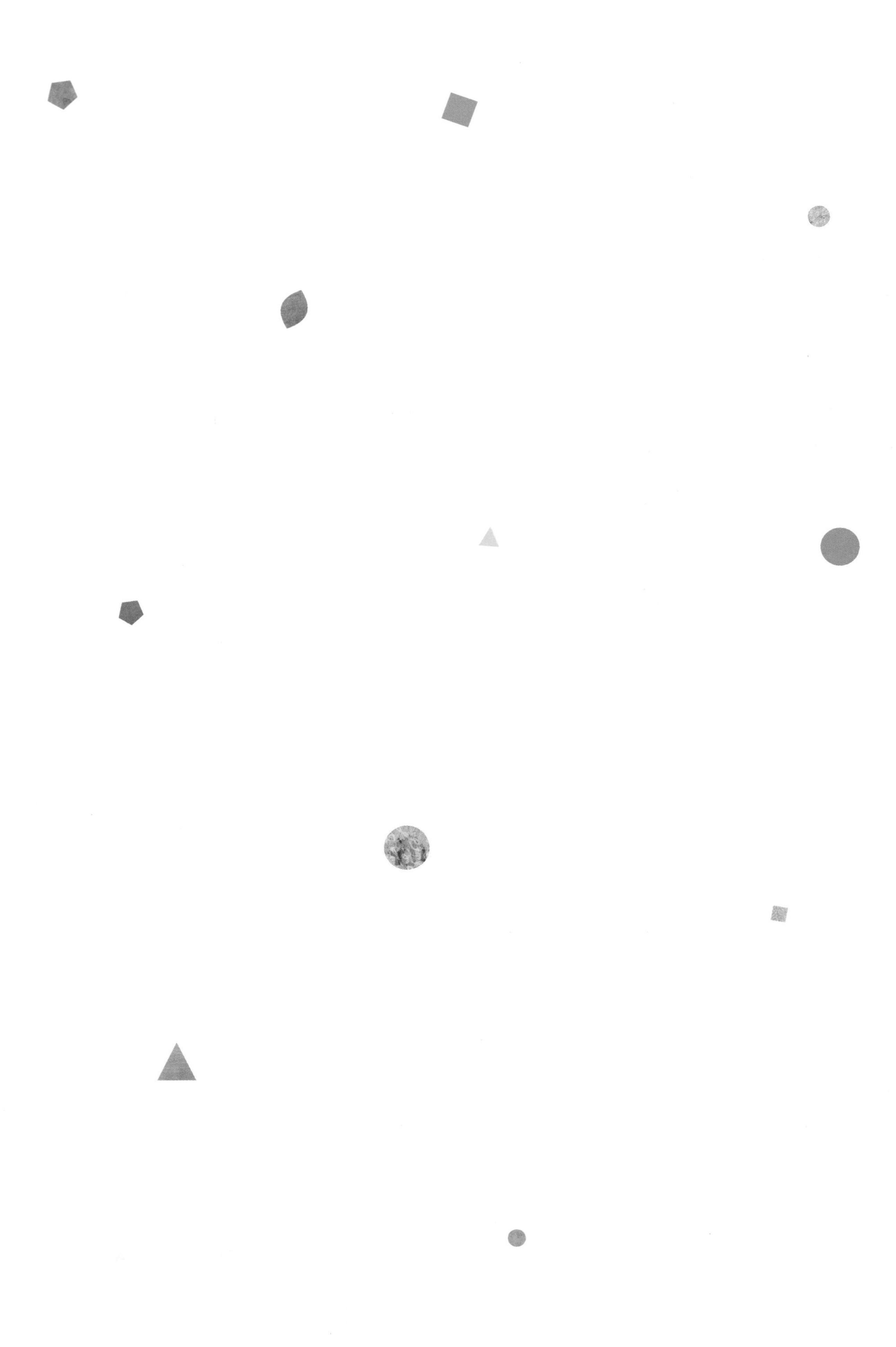

Write the Body (A)

From Outline to Draft

Guided Exercises

Writing with a focus means sticking to the main idea. Keep audience and purpose in mind.

One focus of Lily's Body Paragraph 2 is where the diplodocus lived.

Which facts in Body Paragraph 2 stick to this idea?

Answer the questions about Lily's Report and Lily's Outline.

1. Find the facts in Lily's Outline that tell what the diplodocus ate. Find the same facts in her report. What are they?

   ____

2. Look at the beginning of Lily's Report. Who is her audience?

   ____

3. Find the main idea of Body Paragraph 1 in Lily's Outline. Which sentence in Lily's Report tells the main idea?

   ____

   ____

Try It

Write the Body (A)

Write Your Body

Use your outline to help you write the body of your draft. Write a topic sentence for each paragraph that tells the main idea of that paragraph. Then, write complete sentences to tell each of your facts. Write the facts in the correct order.

Get Ready

Write the Body (B)

Point to Point

Use this list of transition words as you work through the lessons in the unit.

Time

before	soon	then	after	finally
first	next	meanwhile	later	last

Cause and Effect

because	if . . . then	so
for	since	therefore

Importance

most of all	mainly	finally	least of all	too
mostly	as well	lastly	also	

Relationships

although	such as	on the other hand	but
besides	however	for example	
in fact	instead	yet	

Place

above	below	inside	there
across	far	near	within
around	here	outside	

Learn

Write the Body (B)

Use Transitions

Guided Exercises

Use **transitions** to connect ideas in writing.

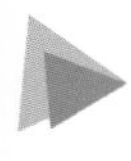

He was a long-necked dinosaur. In fact, he was a diplodocus.

Circle the transition words that Lily used.

WRITING SKILLS

Add a transition word between the two sentences.

1. The dinosaur walked on all four legs. It walked slowly.

____

Add a transition sentence between the sentences.

2. Fossils were found in the Rocky Mountains, Colorado, Montana, Utah, and Wyoming. Diplodocus ate plants.

____

Use Lily's Report to answer the question.

3. What two transitions did Lily use in Body Paragraph 2?

____

Try It

Write the Body (B)

Add Transitions

Continue writing your draft. Remember to add transitions to connect ideas. Write the new sentences. Then, add them to your draft.

WRITING SKILLS

Learn

Introductions

Good Introductions

Guided Exercises

An **introduction** is the beginning of a report. It should grab readers' attention so that they keep reading.

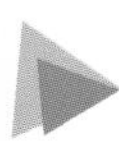

If you like the *Land Before Time* movies, you might know who Doc is.

- Why is this a good introduction?
- Which sentence in the report explains why Lily talks about Doc?

Here are some beginning sentences that can go with a report. Match the opening sentence to the correct topic.

1.	Up, up, and away!	weather
2.	Rain, rain, go away!	how to read maps
3.	"X" marks the spot.	how planes fly
4.	Which side gets the jelly?	how to make a sandwich

Try It

Introductions

Write Your Introduction

Write your introduction. Continue working on your draft.

WRITING SKILLS

Learn

Conclusions

Strong Conclusions

Guided Exercises

A **conclusion** is the final paragraph of the report. It answers readers' questions or states an opinion.

 **Dinosaurs are fun to read about.**

What kind of conclusion did Lily write?

WRITING SKILLS

Write a one-sentence conclusion for each short report.

1. A stegosaurus had a very tiny head. There were bones on its back called plates. It was even larger than an elephant.

____

____

2. Tyrannosaurus Rex was called King of the Dinosaurs. It was the largest and scariest looking of all of the dinosaurs.

____

____

Try It

Conclusions

Write Your Conclusion

Write your conclusion for your report. Add it to your draft. Finish your draft and add a title.

WRITING SKILLS

Conclusions

Tell Me About My Report

Use these questions to get feedback on your report.

1. What is the topic of the report?

   ____

2. Does the report have a main idea? What is it?

   ____

3. Is there a catchy introduction? What is it?

   ____

4. Does each paragraph have a main idea? What are the main ideas?

   ____

5. Are there facts to support the main idea in each paragraph? Where should the writer add facts?

   ____

6. How are the paragraphs and sentences inside the paragraphs organized? Is there time order, order of importance, or logical order?

   ____

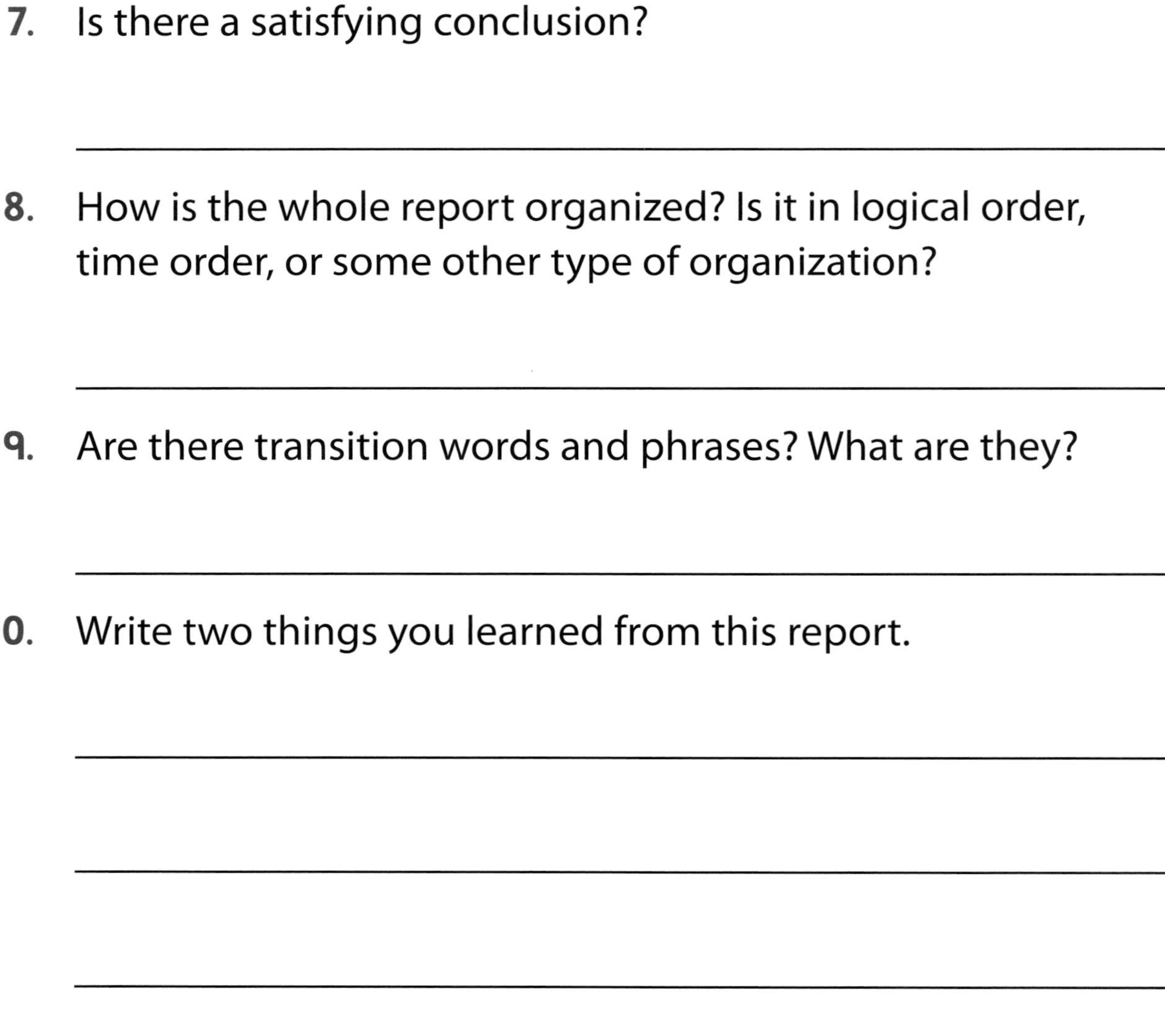

7. Is there a satisfying conclusion?

___

8. How is the whole report organized? Is it in logical order, time order, or some other type of organization?

___

9. Are there transition words and phrases? What are they?

___

10. Write two things you learned from this report.

___

___

___

___

Semester Review: Adjectives, Adverbs, Verb Tenses, and Quotations

Practice Makes Perfect

Choose the adjective that correctly completes the sentence.

neat	rainy	friendly	flat

1. The ______________ dog wagged its tail.

2. You have a really ______________ bedroom!

Choose the answer.

3. Which sentence uses the article correctly?
   A. There is a squirrel in the attic.
   B. There is an squirrel in the attic.

4. Which sentence uses the article correctly?
   A. That's a amazing story!
   B. That's an amazing story!

5. Which sentence has an adverb that tells **when**?
   A. The cupcakes smell great.
   B. I selfishly ate all of the cupcakes.
   C. Nora ate the cupcakes today.
   D. You ate all six cupcakes!

6. Which sentence has an adverb that tells **how**?
   - **A.** The dog howled.
   - **B.** The sad dog howled.
   - **C.** The dog was sad and howling.
   - **D.** The dog howled sadly.

7. Which sentence is written correctly?
   - **A.** I excited opened the gift.
   - **B.** I excitedly opened the gift.

8. Which sentence is written correctly?
   - **A.** A cold wind blew off the bay.
   - **B.** A coldly wind blew off the bay.

9. Which sentence tells about a future action?
   - **A.** Lucy won tonight's race.
   - **B.** Lucy will win tonight's race.
   - **C.** Lucy wins tonight's race.

10. Which sentence tells about a present action?
   - **A.** He mailed the letter.
   - **B.** He will mail the letter.
   - **C.** He mails the letter.

11. Which sentence has a quotation?

   A. Hank told me to wear the red shirt.

   B. Hank said, "Wear the red shirt."

   C. I heard Hank say I should wear the red shirt.

   D. Didn't Hank tell you to wear the red shirt?

Circle the adverb in the sentence.

12. We quickly cleaned the spooky, old house.

Rewrite the underlined verb so that the sentence tells about an action that already happened.

13. I call my sister in Detroit. ________________

14. Four birds sit on the branch. ________________

Place quotation marks where they belong in the sentence.

15. I love pickles on my sandwich, Owen said.

16. The bus driver yelled, Everyone sit down!

WRITING SKILLS

Semester Review: Possessive Nouns, Capital Letters, Commas, and Contractions

Practice Makes Perfect

Circle the possessive noun in the sentence.

1. The hat's brim is bright blue.

Choose the sentence that uses a possessive noun to correctly rewrite the sentence.

2. One of the legs of the bed is shorter than the rest.
   - **A.** One of the beds' legs is shorter than the rest.
   - **B.** One of the beds legs' is shorter than the rest.
   - **C.** One of the bed's legs is shorter than the rest.

Use a possessive noun to replace the underlined words.

3. The cameras the children own are cool.

   The ______________________ cameras are cool.

4. The leaves of the trees are orange and red.

   The ______________________ leaves are orange and red.

Choose the part of the sentence that should have a capital letter.

5. We took the train from boston this morning.
   - **A.** took
   - **B.** train
   - **C.** boston
   - **D.** morning

6. I didn't know uncle Frank was allergic to cheese until today.

A. uncle
B. allergic
C. cheese
D. today

Choose the answer.

7. Which sentence uses capital letters correctly?
   A. Now Dr. Thomas is in Italy.
   B. Now dr. Thomas is in Italy.
   C. Now Dr. thomas is in Italy.
   D. Now Dr. Thomas is in italy.

8. Which sentence uses capital letters correctly?
   A. I will see you on the first Monday of September.
   B. I will see You on the first monday of September.
   C. I will see you on the first Monday of september.
   D. I will see you on the first monday of september.

9. Which sentence uses capital letters correctly?
   A. I ate six oinkers hot dogs on memorial day.
   B. I ate six oinkers hot dogs on Memorial day.
   C. I ate six Oinkers hot dogs on Memorial Day.
   D. I ate six Oinkers hot dogs on memorial Day.

10. Which greeting for a letter is correct?

A. dear mrs. wallace,

B. Dear Mrs. wallace,

C. Dear mrs. Wallace,

D. Dear Mrs. Wallace,

11. Which closing for a letter is correct?

A. Thank You for your time,

B. Thank you for your time,

C. Thank You For Your Time,

Shorten the underlined word correctly.

12. Someone said that Mister Bell was in trouble.

Someone said that ____________________ Bell was in trouble.

Write the initials of the underlined name correctly.

13. The letter is signed Frank Lloyd Wright.

The letter is signed ______________________________.

Place commas where they belong in the sentence.

14. Meg Fred Amy and I walked to the park.

Use contractions to combine the underlined words.

15. You will not know you are lost right away.

You ______________ know ______________ lost right away.

Get Ready

Revise from Feedback

Lily's Draft

Lily wrote her draft on the dinosaur diplodocus. Use Lily's draft as you work through the lessons in the unit.

I like to watch movies. I likes the *Land Before Time* movies. They are fun to watch. I saw a bunch of them. There is a dinosaur called Doc. He has a long neck. He is a diplodocus. What did he look like?

A diplodocus is one of the longest dinosaurs. It had a very long neck. It had a very small head. I dont know how small. It had a long tail. The tail could swing back and forth. It lived in the Rocky Mountains, Colorado, Montana, Utah, and Wyoming. The dinosaur had four legs. It had no arms. It walked on all four legs. I walk a lot.

The diplodocus lived in the Jurassic Period. It lived on land with other dinosaurs. Fossils were found in a lot of places. Another name for that is herbivore. Diplodocus ate plants. It did not choo the plants. It ate them whole?

Dinosaurs are fun to read about. Diplodocus is one of the most interesting of all.

Learn

Revise from Feedback

Focus and Feedback

Guided Exercises

Focus is the direction a piece of writing takes. Delete details that do not stick to the main idea.

I like to watch movies. I likes the *Land Before Time* movies. They are fun to watch. I saw a bunch of them. There is a dinosaur called Doc.

Cross out the sentences that lose focus.

Cross out the sentences that take the writing off track.

A diplodocus is one of the longest dinosaurs. It had a very long neck. It had a very small head. I dont know how small. It had a long tail. The tail could swing back and forth. It lived in the Rocky Mountains, Colorado, Montana, Utah, and Wyoming. The dinosaur had four legs. It had no arms. It walked on all four legs. I walk a lot.

Try It

Revise from Feedback

Use Feedback to Revise

Reread your draft. Revise the focus of your draft. Use the feedback to help you revise.

1. Are there any details in Body Paragraph 1 that do **not** say something about the paragraph's main idea?

   A. Yes **B.** No

2. If you answered Yes, cross out those details with coloring pencils.

3. Are there any details in Body Paragraph 2 that do **not** say something about the paragraph's main idea?

   A. Yes **B.** No

4. If you answered Yes, cross out those sentences with coloring pencils.

5. If you have any more paragraphs, check to see if there are any details in them that **don't** belong.

WRITING SKILLS

Learn

Revise for Content

Revise Content

Guided Exercises

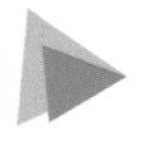

Content is ideas and details in a piece of writing. Revise for content by adding facts and information.

Its teeth were shaped like pencils.

This sentence was not in Lily's Draft. Why did Lily add it to Paragraph 1?

Use Lily's Draft and Lily's Report to answer the questions about Lily's revisions.

1. Lily got feedback asking why the diplodocus needed to swing its tail. What sentence did Lily add to her draft to answer this question?

____

2. One of Lily's readers asked her to find out more about how diplodocus walked. What sentence did Lily add to answer this question?

____

3. Lily got feedback asking her to add facts about other dinosaurs that lived during the same time period. What dinosaur names did she add to her report?

____

WRITING SKILLS

Try It

Revise for Content

Revise Your Ideas

Reread your draft. Revise the content of your draft. Use the feedback you received to help you revise.

1. Are there any ideas you could add to Body Paragraph 1?

   A. Yes **B.** No

2. If you answered Yes, add the facts to your draft with coloring pencils.

3. Are there any ideas you could add to Body Paragraph 2?

   A. Yes **B.** No

4. If you answered Yes, add the facts to your draft with coloring pencils.

5. If you have any additional paragraphs, are there any ideas you could add to them?

   A. Yes **B.** No

6. If you answered Yes, add the facts to your draft with coloring pencils.

7. Write any new sentences on your draft.

Learn

Revise for Organization

Review Organization

Guided Exercises

Organization in writing is both the order of the paragraphs and the order of the information within each paragraph.

It lived in the Rocky Mountains, Colorado, Montana, Utah, and Wyoming.

This sentence was in Body Paragraph 1 in Lily's Draft. Why did she move it?

Answer the questions about Lily's Report and Lily's Draft.

1. In Lily's Report, she added a new sentence: "Also, it stood on its back legs and ate tall plants." Where did she put it?

____

2. Does the sentence belong there? Why?

____

3. In Lily's Draft, she wrote: "Another name for that is herbivore. Diplodocus ate plants." Are her sentences in the correct order? Why?

____

Try It

Revise for Organization

Revise Organization

Reread your draft. Revise the organization of your draft. Use the feedback you received to help you revise.

1. Are the paragraphs in the correct order?

   A. Yes **B.** No

2. If you answered No, number the paragraphs in order on your draft.

3. Are there any sentences that are in the wrong paragraph?

   A. Yes **B.** No

4. If you answered Yes, draw an arrow on your draft to show where they should go.

5. Are there any sentences within your paragraphs that are in the wrong order?

   A. Yes **B.** No

6. If you answered Yes, draw an arrow to show the correct order.

7. Do you need to add transitions to any sentences to have them make sense? If so, mark them in your draft.

Learn

Proofread and Polish Your Report

Proofread and Polish

Guided Exercises

Proofread your work to look for errors.

I likes the *Land Before Time* movies.

- Lily used the checklist and found an error in this sentence.
- Find the error and correct it.

Find Lily's errors and fix them.

1. I dont know how small.
2. It did not choo the plants.
3. It ate them whole?

Combine the sentences.

4. It had a very long neck. It had a very small head.

____

____

WRITING SKILLS

Try It

Proofread and Polish Your Report

Final Checklist

Use the checklist to proofread and polish your report. Use coloring pencils to fix the errors on your draft.

- ☐ Does my report have a title?
- ☐ Are my sentences complete?
- ☐ Did I use nouns, pronouns, verbs, and adjectives correctly?
- ☐ Do my verbs agree with their subjects?
- ☐ Do my sentences have correct punctuation?
- ☐ Did I capitalize proper nouns and the first word in a sentence?
- ☐ Are apostrophes used correctly in contractions and possessives?
- ☐ Did I indent my paragraphs?
- ☐ Can my sentences be combined for variety?
- ☐ Did I use a dictionary to check my spelling?
- ☐ Did I use a thesaurus to find stronger words?

Write Now

Publish Your Report

Final Copy

Complete the clean, final copy of your report. Draw a picture on a separate page to illustrate your report.

WRITING SKILLS

WRITING SKILLS

Peer Interaction

Publish Your Report

Tell Me About My Presentation

Have another person answer these questions and give you feedback on your presentation.

1. Did the presenter speak loudly and clearly?

____

2. Did the presenter make eye contact with the audience?

____

3. Did the presenter speak smoothly and sound prepared?

____

4. Did the presentation include an introduction and a conclusion?

____

____

5. Was the order of ideas easy to follow? If not, what idea seemed out of place?

____

____

WRITING SKILLS

6. Did the presentation have an illustration or another visual? What was it? Did it connect to the presentation?

____

____

7. Did the presenter speak with enthusiasm?

____

8. How could the presentation be improved?

____

____

____

____

____

____

____

____